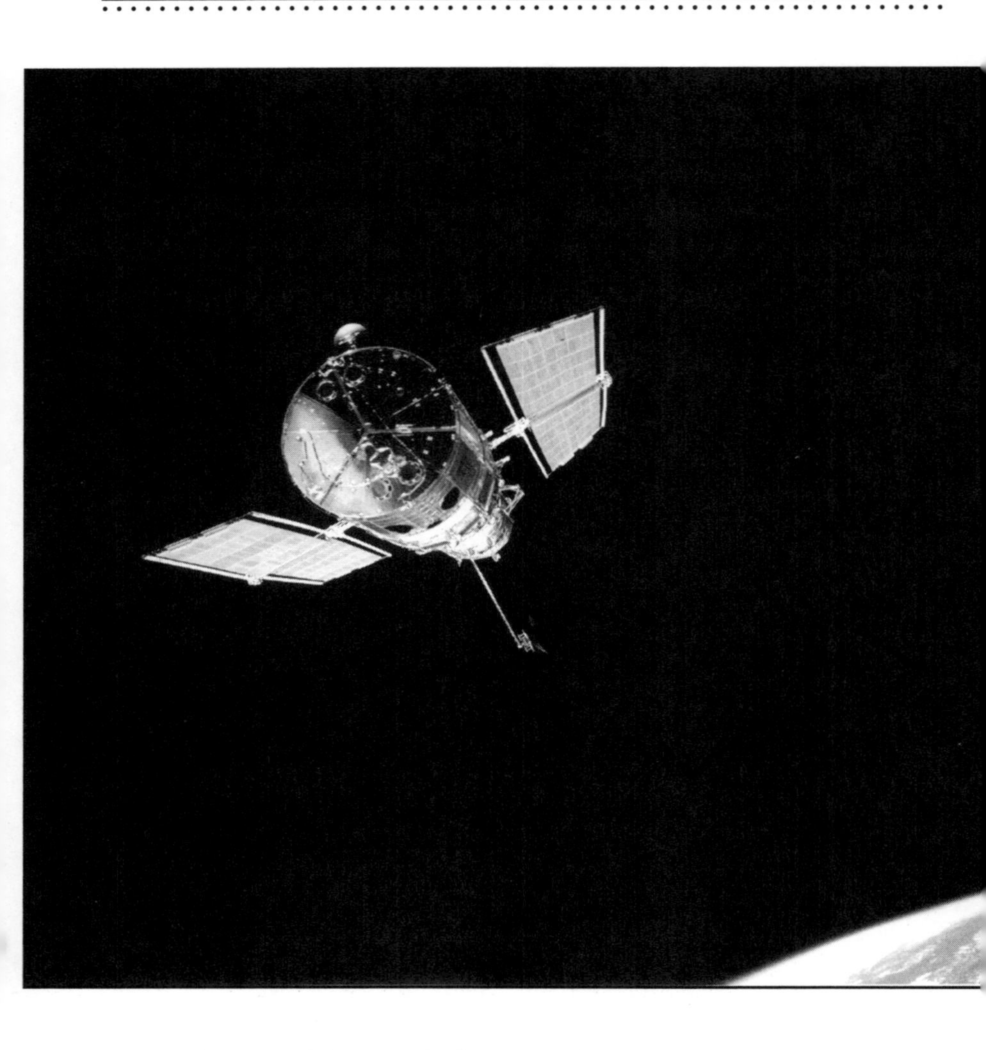

OTHER SCIENTIFIC AMERICAN FOCUS BOOKS

Medication of the Mind

Cosmic Collisions

The Language of Animals

Of Mind and Body

The New Media and the Future of Communications

THE STRUCTURE OF THE UNIVERSE

PAUL HALPERN

Foreword by Bruce Gregory

A SCIENTIFIC AMERICAN FOCUS BOOK

Henry Holt and Company
New York

Henry Holt and Company, Inc.
Publishers since 1866
115 West 18th Street
New York, New York 10011

Henry Holt® is a registered trademark
of Henry Holt and Company, Inc.

Published in Canada by Fitzhenry & Whiteside Ltd.
195 Allstate Parkway, Markham, Ontario L3R 4T8.

Library of Congress Cataloging-in-Publication Data
Halpern, Paul.
The structure of the universe / Paul Halpern;
foreword by Bruce Gregory.
p. cm.—(Scientific American focus book)
"An Owl Book."
Includes bibliographical references and index.
1. Cosmology. I. Title. II. Series 96-40993
QB981.H27 1996

ISBN 0-8050-4028-5
ISBN 0-8050-4029-3 (An Owl Book: pbk.)

Henry Holt books are available for special promotions
and premiums. For details contact: Director, Special markets.

First edition—1997

Photo credits are on page 128.

Editorial and production services: G&H SOHO, Inc., Hoboken, NJ

Printed in the United States of America
All first editions are printed
on acid-free paper.

10 9 8 7 6 5 4 3 2 1
10 9 8 7 6 5 4 3 2 1 (pbk.)

To *Max Dresden,* for his insights and stories

ACKNOWLEDGMENTS

any thanks to Robert Ubell, Scott Veggeberg, Luis Gonzalez, Barbara Sullivan, and David Sobel for their useful suggestions for this project. Thanks to the faculty and staff of the Philadelphia College of Pharmacy and Science for their strong encouragement. I also appreciate the generous support and advice of my wife, Felicia Hurewitz.

CONTENTS

F O R E W O R D

he telescopes atop Mount Hopkins in the Sonoran Desert are not the largest or the most sophisticated in the world, but with them my colleagues at the Harvard–Smithsonian Center for Astrophysics (CfA) have made major advances in our understanding of the nature and history of the universe. How they did this provides one small picture of the way astronomers are answering the questions that have puzzled human beings since our ancestors first looked up into the night sky.

John Huchra is one of the most successful hunters of galaxies astronomy has ever known. Most of the galaxies Huchra observes are simply smudges of light, but he somehow manages to have a relationship with each one. Each galaxy that John observes is added to a map that slowly reveals the distribution of visible matter in the nearby universe.

Huchra and his partner, Margaret Geller, have different personalities, but work well together. Huchra loves to observe and Geller excels at planning and analysis. Together they have made a substantial impact on our understanding of the universe at large. Before Geller joined Huchra there had been several efforts at mapping the universe, but these had provided no compelling results. Geller suggested a new approach to mapping the galaxies—concentrate the effort on a thin slice extending more than a quarter of the way around the celestial sphere, but only a few degrees wide. She was convinced that this approach would best reveal how galaxies are distributed in the nearby universe.

Huchra and Geller assigned the task of plotting each new observation to a graduate student as part of her doctoral project. Huchra was primarily concerned with making the observations, but why was Geller not interested enough to plot the data as Huchra gathered it? The Russian scientist Ya Zel'dovich had proposed a picture in which matter first collapsed into giant pancakes that later fragmented into the galaxies we see today. The distribution of the galaxies we observe should provide evidence for the existence of those primordial pancakes. Geller's mentor at Princeton, Jim Peebles, on the other hand, proposed a picture in which galaxies formed first and only later gathered into larger collections. Geller's studies of the statistics of galaxies had convinced her that Peebles was right. She believed that the best the CfA survey could do would be to burst the bubble of the giant-pancake theory by demonstrating that the universe does not have large-scale structure. So six months after Huchra had gathered the data from frequent visits to Mount Hopkins, it was left for Valerie de

Lapperant to see for the first time the structure revealed by the CfA survey. When she reported her results to Huchra, he recalls that his first reaction was to wonder what he and his fellow astronomists had done wrong.

The CfA survey extended to fainter and therefore sometimes more distant galaxies (since a galaxy that appears faint to us may be less luminous or at a greater distance from Earth). The survey contained less than half the number of galaxies in an earlier CfA survey, but the galaxies were confined to a small strip across the sky. The results of the second CfA survey proved to be a bombshell. The survey showed a slice of the universe seemingly filled with voids. Indeed, galaxies appeared confined largely to thin shells surrounding these giant voids. The edge of the largest void in the survey is shown to be remarkably sharp, not at all what one might have expected from the clumping produced by gravity that Peebles suggested.

The "bubble-structure" caused something of a sensation when de Lapperant, Geller, and Huchra published their findings in 1986. Earlier studies had hinted at the existence of galaxies in large sheets and of voids, but the second CfA survey unmistakably showed them. How did these giant bubbles come into being? What are they telling us about the history and fate of the universe?

The bubble-structure of the universe is only one of the discoveries of modern astronomy Paul Halpern describes in this engaging and readable book. With his guidance you will explore the findings that have shaped our view of the contents, extent, and history of the universe, as well as the question of its ultimate fate. The results he interprets represent advances of knowledge comparable to those reaped by the voyagers during the age of discovery in the fifteenth and sixteenth centuries. The age of the universe, the manner of its birth, and its ultimate fate, like the continents of North and South America, can be discovered only once. The breakthroughs astronomers are making today provide a riveting picture of the universe that is our home. We live in a truly unique time. It is not hard to imagine that hundreds of years from now people will look back on our time as the greatest age of discovery humanity has ever known. You are fortunate to have so knowledgeable and helpful a guide as Paul Halpern to these exciting times.

—Bruce Gregory
Harvard-Smithsonian Center for Astrophysics

Mysteries of Space

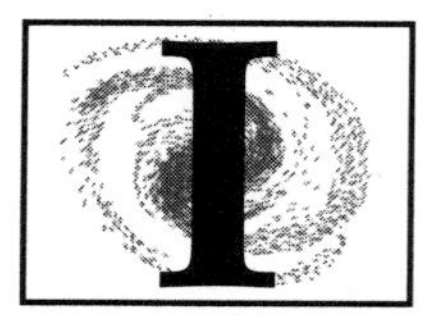
Imagine that you wake up one day and find yourself stranded in a small boat, slowly making its way across a vast uncharted sea. Nothing around you offers a clue as to how or why you've come to be on this vessel. You suspect somehow that you will be there, all alone, for a very long time.

You look around inside the boat's cabin and find a wide array of useful items. These include a pair of binoculars, a considerable reserve of food and water, a desalination device, and other essential supplies. Realizing that it could be a while until you are off the boat, you pick up the binoculars, walk out onto the deck, and begin searching for signs of land.

As you scan the ocean with the binoculars, the expanse seems at first to be empty—vast and featureless. However, as you manage to adjust your viewing instrument to more precise settings, you start to observe distinct signs of structure around you. Here and there, bits of rock and pieces of coral jut out from the placid blue surface. The appearances of these formations vary; some are tall and craggy, while others are smooth and squat. Their colors range from shell-white hues to shiny jet-black tones.

At first these structures seem to be randomly distributed throughout the waters. However, as you survey the ocean more closely, detailed manner, you note unmistakable evidence of order. Some of the coral clumps, for example, seem to be organized into long sinuous reefs. They form complex serpentine patterns throughout the sea. You also note that some of the distant rock formations appear to comprise the borders and interiors of small islands. The patterns presented by these reefs and islands break up the sheer monotony of the mostly uniform surroundings.

Soon you discover a new binocular setting, one that enlarges the scope's range and sharpens its focus. Now you can peer out even farther than before and observe additional features that you missed earlier. The reefs, you find, are mainly oriented in the same direction—what you take arbitrarily to be east to west rather than what you consider to be north to south. The islands also form patterns; they are grouped in clusters. These clusters, in turn, form intricate archipelagos, strung out across the waters like pearls on necklaces.

For weeks and weeks you continue your survey. As time goes on you observe more and more signs of structure all around. You record thousands of single islands, reefy barriers, island chains, chains of island chains, etc. The sea around you seems to be a far more complex place than the barren expanse you first suspected it was.

Finally, your probe reaches its limit; you can see no farther. Still, many questions remain, untouched by your search. For instance, does the sea go on forever, or is it bounded by continents? And what are the origins of the intricate patterns around you? Why are the islands grouped in clusters and the reefs mainly oriented in the same direction? It will take some doing to find the answers to these riddles—but you have plenty of time, no doubt.

Our cosmic sailing ship, the Earth, glides rapidly through the vast ocean of space. At present we are stranded on this vessel, and we are fated to ride with it on the twisting currents of gravity. We are profoundly alone; Earth's nearest neighbors, Venus and Mars, are millions of miles away. Furthermore, the closest life-sustaining planets are likely hundreds of trillions of miles away.

Someday humankind will develop the ability to span the enormous distances between the stars. Until then, our main source of information about the structure of the universe comes from scanning the skies. This is a serious limitation. Nevertheless, by using telescopes and other imaging devices we have learned a great deal over the ages about the nature of space.

Our view of the universe keeps changing. As viewing instruments have improved, our knowledge of the structure of our surroundings has grown richer. Once the cosmos was thought of as small (relatively speaking), static, and fathomable. Now, it is considered vast, mutable, and in many ways, incomprehensible. The magnitude of this change in viewpoint is simply staggering to ponder.

Historically, triggered by the development of better optical instruments, three major revolutions have taken place in our attempts to picture space. The first, led by Galileo (among others) in the seventeenth century, wrested the Earth from its ancient pedestal in the center of the

William Herschel's 40-foot telescope, 1789.

heavens. Galileo aimed his early telescope at the stars and planets, mapping them out and proving that our world occupies a small fraction of space. During the eighteenth and nineteenth centuries, astronomers firmed up Galileo's findings by scanning the skies and developing an increasingly detailed map of an eternal, star-speckled universe.

Then, in the early twentieth century, another monumental change in thinking took place, stimulated by the development of larger sky-searching instruments such the Hooker telescope on Mount Wilson, near Los Angeles. There, Edwin Hubble proved what a number of astronomers had suspected—that the stars in space are grouped into much larger units called *galaxies*. Our own galaxy, the Milky Way, is but one of many. He further found that the bulk of the galaxies in the cosmos appear to be moving away from each other at enormous speeds.

Later, scientists concluded from this and other evidence that the universe once occupied the space of a point, and that it expanded outward from this speck in a "burst" called the *Big Bang*. Most astronomers date this event roughly 15 or 20 billion years in the past, long enough ago to accommodate even the oldest stars.

Today, on the cusp of the twenty-first century, a third major revolution is brewing—one leading, perhaps, to a rethinking of the Big Bang model. In this case, the telescopes providing the results critical for this restructuring are a diverse lot. They range from the mammoth ground-based Keck telescope on Mauna Kea in Hawaii to new rocket-launched devices, such

The Keck Telescope on Mauna Kea, Hawaii, the largest telescope in the world.

as the Hubble Space Telescope, as well as balloon probes, radio dishes, and a host of other exotic instruments.

These light-recording devices are telling us strange and at times seemingly conflicting things about space. In 1994, Wendy Freedman and several of her colleagues at the Carnegie Institute in Pasadena, California, used the Hubble Telescope to measure the age of the universe. The technique they employed involved measuring the distance from Earth to a grouping of galaxies known as the Virgo Cluster, and then using this information to estimate the current rate of the universe's expansion. From this expansion rate, they calculated how long it has been since the initial

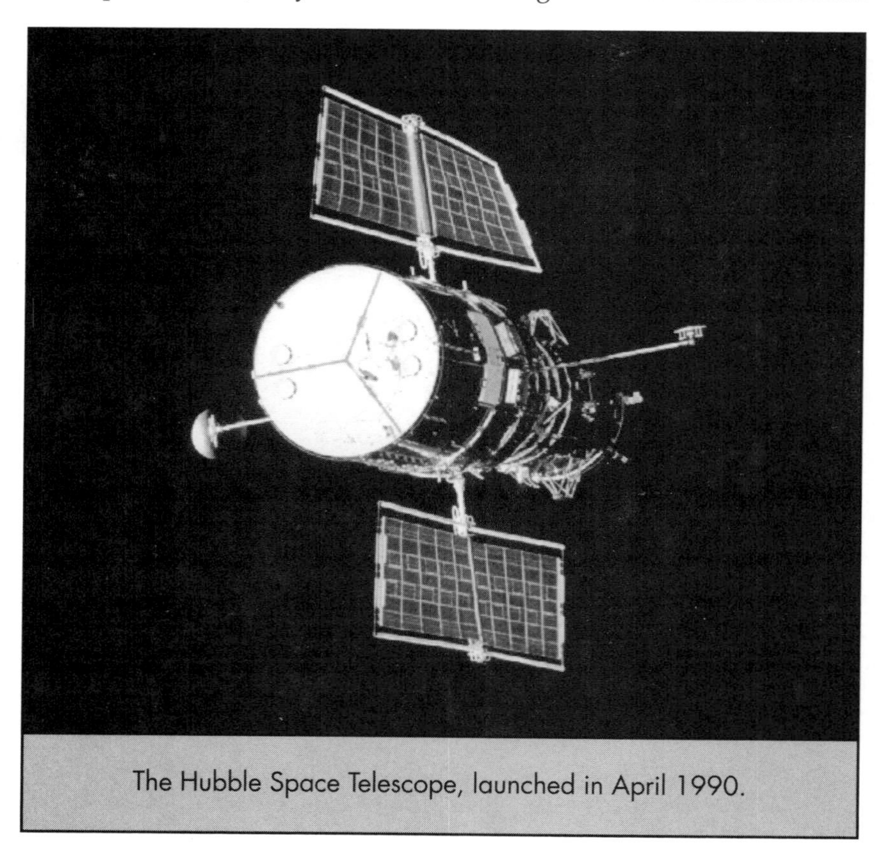

The Hubble Space Telescope, launched in April 1990.

"blast" of the Big Bang. Astonishingly they found evidence that the cosmos is quite young—according to their estimate, between 8 and 12 billion years. This is less than the age of many stars. Now, researchers are scrambling to develop models of the cosmos that could account for this discrepancy. The age question—the problem of reconciling seemingly incompatible astronomical time scales—has become one of the leading sources of debate in cosmology.

And that is not all. Gargantuan structures have been found across space—cosmic bubbles, walls, and voids. An area in the sky has been discovered, called the Great Attractor, that inexplicably draws galaxies in the region toward it. Black holes have been recorded in the centers of galaxies, and MACHOs (massive compact halo objects) of unknown content have been seen in galactic peripheries. Scientists' estimates of the number of galaxies in the universe have recently grown fivefold, from 10 billion to 50 billion. Furthermore, it has become clear in the past few years that the bulk of the universe is composed of material that gives off no detectable light. One can only speculate what the ancients would have said if they had known that most of the matter in the cosmos is invisible.

The road from Babylonian astrology to modern cosmology, from the astrolabe to the Hubble Space Telescope, and from Pythagoras to Wendy Freedman is long and twisty indeed. There have been many detours, dead ends, and other divergences along the way. Therefore, before discussing contemporary notions of the nature of the cosmos, let's start at the beginning of cosmological history and discern how our ancestors first began to map out the universe.

The Parade of Planets

e do not know who among the ancients was the first to discover the planets. (The word *planet* itself comes from the ancient Greek *planetes* and means "wanderer.") We can only assume that at some point in history, observers distinguished the behavior of the planets from that of the "fixed stars." It was noted that while ordinary stars seem to move in unison from night to night, the planets appear to track out independent paths. One might say, then, that the unknown people who first noticed this fact were the true discoverers of the planets.

This distinction can be seen by noting that while star patterns, such as the Big Dipper, are essentially stable (in the course of hundreds of years at least) with respect to the stellar background, planets, such as Mars and Jupiter, tend to shift around in the sky. If you stand at a given site in the Northern Hemisphere and look up at the sky, the Big Dipper always appears to be surrounded by the same set of stars. On the other hand, Mars and Jupiter continuously move around the heavens, both with respect to the stars and with respect to each other. These planets might appear close together on one date and far apart months later.

Ancient civilizations believed that the relative positions of the planets influenced events on Earth. Disasters, such as wars, fires, floods, and famines, could be predicted, they thought, by carefully analyzing and interpreting planetary motions. Therefore, early astrologers kept careful records of these movements and periodically issued dire warnings about imminent catastrophes.

The arrival of a conjunction, when two or more planets appear close to each other, was seen as an especially powerful omen. The more planets that were lined up for a particular conjunction, the rarer it was, and the more significance it was assigned by the ancients.

The most detailed early scientific portrait of planetary behavior was developed by the ancient Greeks during the sixth through fourth century B.C. At that time, classical Greek philosophers such as Pythagoras, Plato, and Aristotle imagined that the planets (along with the Sun, Moon, and stars) circle the Earth periodically. Pythagoras and Plato attributed this rhythmic behavior to the mathematical regularity of nature, the same sort of harmony represented by the tonal scales of music and the patterns of planar geometry. Aristotle viewed the movements of the celestial bodies as part of a clockwork physical order, set into motion by a Creator. While the cosmologies of Pythagoras and Plato included metaphysical components, and the universe of Aristotle basically did not, each shared a vision of a concentric series of perfect circular orbits, with the Earth as center.

The Greek philosopher Pythagoras viewed the cosmos as a musical scale.

These early geocentric (Earth-centered) models of planetary motion were far from accurate. They share the assumption that each planet completes a uniform, circular orbit around the Earth. However, in reality, planets do not always appear to trace out one-way paths in the heavens. Rather, they often seem to reverse their directions of motion—moving forward, then backward, then forward again. These reversals take place periodically, and cannot be accounted for by simple circular orbit theories.

To explain this phenomenon, called *retrograde motion,* the Greek scholar Apollonius of Perga developed, in the third century B.C., a more intricate model of the planets. According to this theory, planets execute smaller circles in space, called *epicycles,* while following large circular paths around the Earth. The combination of these circuits accounts for periodic reversals of direction.

Ancient Greek notions of astronomy remained prevalent throughout Europe and North Africa for centuries, up until the end of the Middle Ages. These ideas were summarized in the book *Almagest* (meaning

Astronomy, 1533.

"The Great System" in Arabic), written in the second century A.D. by Ptolemy of Alexandria.

Ptolemy's work, a synthesis of classical knowledge along with some of his own ideas, was seen by medieval scholars as the authoritative account of celestial behavior. It advocated a geocentric model of the planets, including the epicycles of Apollonius, as well as additional geometric elements, called eccentrics (deviations of orbital centers from Earth) and equants (off-center points about which the epicycles move). These complex schemes were included to reproduce observed planetary behavior. In contrast to the intricate orbits of the planets, however, the Sun, Moon, and stars were seen as revolving around the Earth along simple circular paths.

Because of the influence of the Ptolemaic approach, for hundreds of years the Earth was considered to be the physical center of the cosmos, surrounded by a complex array of orbiting bodies. This was the state of affairs until the Renaissance, when a supreme revolution in cosmological thought took place. In this monumental change of perspective, the Earth was dethroned and replaced on its pedestal by the Sun. From that time on, no longer was our planet considered the crux of the universe.

The first important advocate of a heliocentric (Sun-centered) cosmology was the sixteenth-century Polish astronomer Nicholas Copernicus. Copernicus was puzzled by the conflict between the elaborate Ptolemaic system and the Platonic ideal of simple circles. To resolve this contradiction, he revived the ideas of another, less well known, Greek philosopher, Aristarchus, who had written in the third century B.C. that the Earth revolves around the Sun.

After years of careful calculations and ruminations about the implications of a heliocentric universe, Copernicus released in 1543 his most important work, *Revolutions of the Celestial Spheres.* In this treatise, printed shortly before his death, he advanced the view that Earth and the five then-known planets follow simple circular paths around the Sun. To explain the appearance of the stars as "fixed," he stated that they occupy a spherical shell, centered on the Sun, well beyond the domain of the planets. Finally, he wrote that the Moon alone orbits the Earth.

Nicholas Copernicus (1473–1573), Polish astronomer.

The Copernican system was considered blasphemous by the Church, which had cast its long shadow over science for quite some time. Because of Christian teachings that the Earth is the sole realm of the physical, and the heavens, that of the spiritual, the Church had firmly aligned itself with the

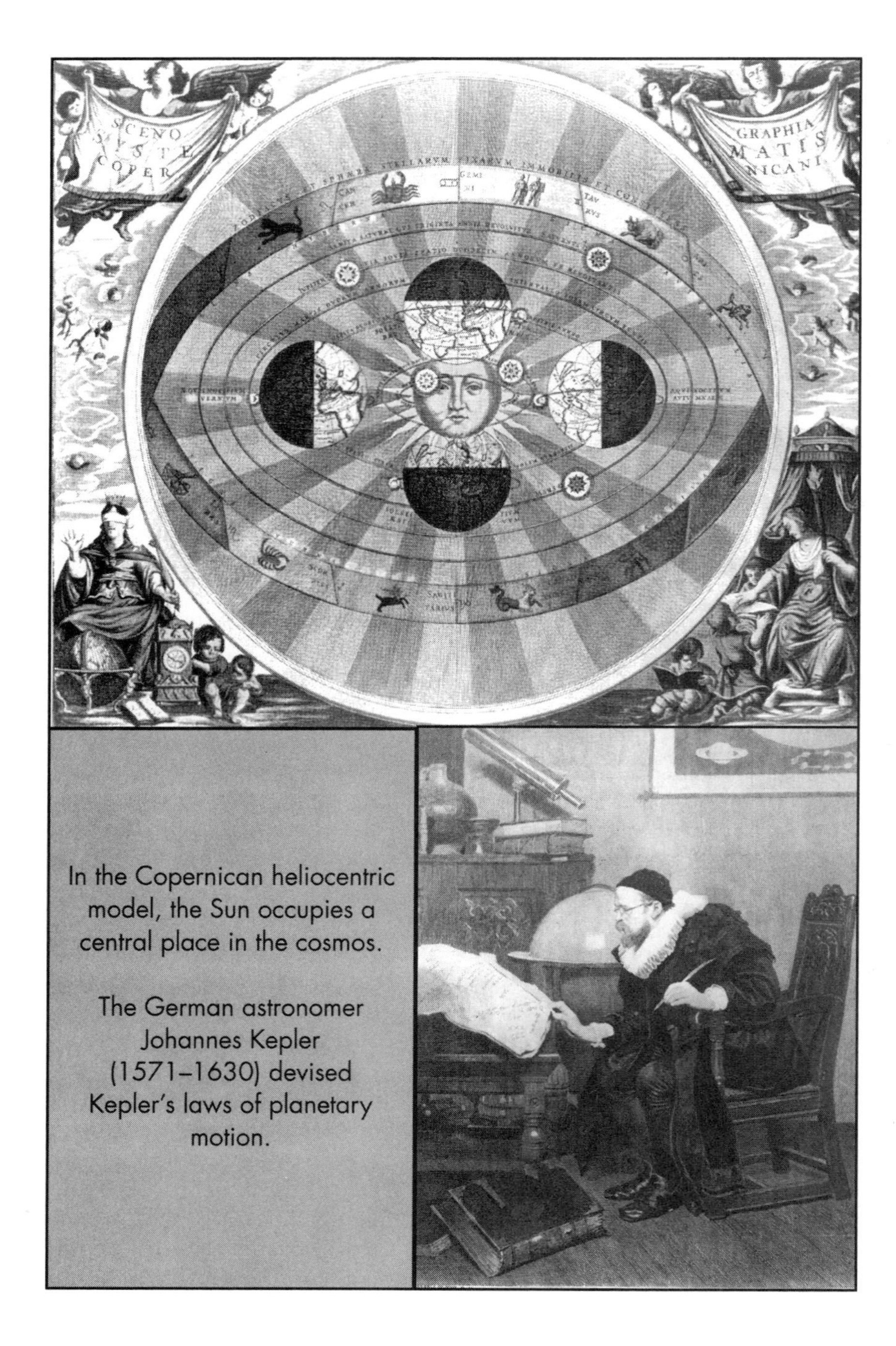

In the Copernican heliocentric model, the Sun occupies a central place in the cosmos.

The German astronomer Johannes Kepler (1571–1630) devised Kepler's laws of planetary motion.

geocentric viewpoint, particularly with the cosmology of Aristotle. By placing the Earth on a par with the other planets, Copernicus implied that these other bodies were physical as well. The Earth ceased to occupy a special place in cosmology. Naturally, this was too much for the Church to accept, and the writings of Copernicus were condemned.

Challenging the doctrine of the Church, Italian philosopher Giordano Bruno published in 1584 the book *Of Infinity, the Universe and the World,* advocating a Copernican view of the cosmos. Bruno took Copernicus one step further, arguing that not only is there a planetary system around the Sun but that there is one around each of the stars. Moreover, he wrote that the number of stars and planets in the universe is infinite. He did not provide tangible evidence for his hypothesis, but rather employed spiritual arguments to make his case. The Church was even more hostile to Bruno's ideas than it was to those of Copernicus. In 1600, for his heretical beliefs, Bruno was burned at the stake in Rome.

The ideas of Copernicus and Bruno were speculative rather than empirical. Neither philosopher proved definitively that the Earth and planets orbit the Sun; observational evidence was needed to establish their case. Moreover, to make detailed predictions of orbital behavior, a mathematical description of the movements of planets was required. Finally, to link the rules governing planetary motions with those concerning terrestrial interactions, a new set of physical laws needed to be stated. These requirements were adroitly satisfied in the seventeenth century by Galileo, Kepler, and Newton, respectively.

Galileo Galilei was born in Pisa in 1564. In his youth, his scientific productivity was remarkable. While a student at the University of Pisa, he made a number of important discoveries, including the fact that a pendulum of a given length swings at a constant rate, regardless of how far it is initially displaced from its balance point. (According to legend, it was also at Pisa where he performed a simple gravity experiment—dropping two objects, each of different mass, off the Leaning Tower to show that they fall at the same rate.)

In 1592, Galileo left the University of Pisa and was appointed Chair of Mathematics at the University of Padua. The next eighteen years represented the most productive period of his life. His work in dynamics, the science of moving bodies, brought him great renown. But it was his astronomical findings that would make the greatest impact upon science.

The Trial of Galileo

Galileo's treatise on astronomy, *Dialogue on the Two Great World Systems,* was to change forever the way humankind viewed the cosmos, banishing the false idea that the Earth is the center of the universe. But to the Church authorities in Italy it was a heretical document, written in contempt of an order they had given to Galileo in 1616, specifically forbidding him to discuss Copernican notions. For his disobedience of this edict he was brought before the Inquisition in 1633.

Historians generally agree that Galileo would have been spared if he hadn't been openly contemptuous of those who supported Earth-centered cosmologies. Unfortunately, Galileo had referred in his book to his powerful opponents as "mental pygmies," "dumb idiots," and "hardly deserving to be called human beings." Naturally, this angered the Church even more.

At the trial, a panic-stricken Galileo claimed that he had refuted, rather than supported, Copernicus in his writings. The Inquisition court was hardly convinced by Galileo's denials. The evidence to convict him was omnipresent. Finally, Galileo was pressed to admit that his book could be construed by some readers as Copernican. He apologized for this "oversight" and offered to amend the book.

With a primitive telescope of his own construction, Galileo mapped out the appearance and behavior of celestial bodies to an unprecedented extent. He discovered mountains on the Moon and satellites orbiting Jupiter. He resolved hundreds of stars, recorded the phases of Venus, and plotted out the motions of sunspots. He published his work in 1610 in a book called *The Starry Messenger.*

Galileo's extensive research led him to realize that the observed planets and the Moon shared with Earth a number of similar features. He was thereby persuaded to place these celestial bodies on equal footing with each other (more or less)—considering each to be a physical world in its own right. He concluded that the Copernican heliocentric model,

Galileo: Inquisition scene.

Faced with a humbled Galileo, the Inquisition pushed no further. It dealt him a relatively light sentence (as Inquisitional punishments went). Galileo spent his last years under house arrest, and never wrote again on cosmology. In 1992, 350 years after his death, he was exonerated by Pope John Paul II.

rather than the Ptolemaic or Aristotlean approach, would best describe this "democratic" state of affairs. He announced his support for the views of Copernicus in the book *Dialogue on the Two Great World Systems*, published in 1632. When he died in 1642, the power of his written arguments was already beginning to persuade the bulk of the European astronomical community that the Earth revolves around the Sun.

One of Galileo's trusted correspondents was the German scientist Johannes Kepler. Kepler shared with Galileo a strong belief in Copernican cosmology. Unlike Galileo, however, Kepler espoused his beliefs openly and never wavered in his expressed convictions.

Kepler was born in 1571 in the town of Weil der Stadt, then part of the Holy Roman Empire. Trained in theology and mathematics, in 1601 he was fortunate enough to succeed Tycho Brahe as imperial mathematician in Prague. When Kepler assumed this position, he gained access to several decades worth of naked-eye astronomical measurements of the planets taken by Brahe.

Over the years, Kepler compiled and analyzed this wealth of data, seeking to prove the Copernican description of planetary motion. In particular, he tried to show that the orbit of Mars was a circle around the Sun. But as much as he tried, he couldn't find a circular path that would match up with Brahe's values. He discovered, however, that the orbit of Mars was well matched by a geometric figure called an *ellipse.* An ellipse is an oval-shaped object with precise mathematical characteristics. Specifically, it is defined in terms of two internal points, called *foci,* such that the sum of the distance from any given point of the ellipse to one focus plus the distance from that point to the other focus is a constant. After further study, Kepler found that the orbits of each of the then-known planets could be described as ellipses in which the Sun was one of the foci. Thus, he showed that, rather than resembling a series of concentric circles, the orbits of the bodies in the solar system were all ellipses, and all shared one of their two foci, the Sun.

Although Kepler provided science with a mathematically perfect

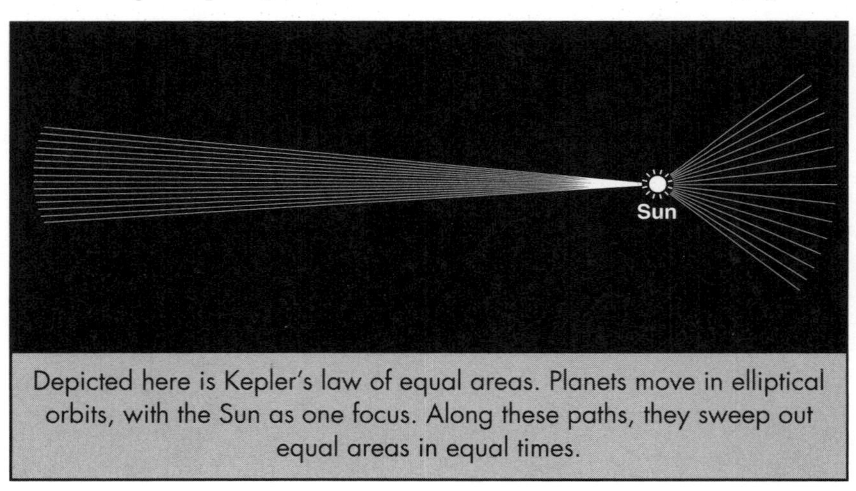

Depicted here is Kepler's law of equal areas. Planets move in elliptical orbits, with the Sun as one focus. Along these paths, they sweep out equal areas in equal times.

description of *how* planets move, he failed to explain *why* they move that way. This latter task was carried out by a man considered by many to be one of the greatest scientists of all time, Isaac Newton.

Newton was born in Woolsthorpe, England, in the year of Galileo's death. During his long scientific career, mainly as a professor of mathematics at Cambridge University, he made substantial, and often pivotal, contributions to the fields of mathematics, physics, and astronomy.

Perhaps Newton is best known for his theory of universal gravitation. Legend has it that his interest in the phenomenon of gravity began when he noticed an apple falling from a tree. Supposedly, he then began to wonder about the nature of the force attracting bodies to one another. Soon he realized that the same pull that draws an apple down to Earth also draws the Moon toward Earth, and Earth toward the Sun.

Newton encapsulated his gravitational theories, as well as other principles of dynamics, in his treatise *Principia.* In this book, he proved that the elliptical orbits of the planets around the Sun could be predicted by a simple mathematical equation. This law states that the gravitational force between bodies depends inversely on the square of the distance between them. In other words, the closer two objects are, the greater the gravitational attraction, by a factor of the square of the amount of separation. By combining this law of universal gravitation with his laws of motion (also stated in *Principia),* and applying these principles to the case of the interaction of any given planet with the Sun, Newton showed that the planet would travel in a simple ellipse with the Sun as one focus.

Newton's laws forever changed the science of cosmology. Before Newton, the study of the universe was considered a metaphysical venture. Unable to make predictions based on firm mathematical principles, early scientists needed to use faith and intuition to explain the motions of the planets and stars. Newtonian cosmology, on the other hand, requires no recourse to theology. It embodies a clockwork vision of the universe in which each component is related to every other component through precise equations.

Since the time of Newton, astronomers have discovered three more planets in the solar system: Uranus, Neptune, and Pluto. Like the inner six, these outer planets engage in roughly elliptical orbits. However, scientists now know that the paths traced by planets are not *exact* ellipses. Following the law of gravity, the planets are not just attracted by the

Sun; they are also drawn by each other. Therefore, each planet's trajectory is affected by the gravitational influences of all the others. These mutual attractions are strongest when planets are closest together, and show up as "wobbles" in planetary orbits.

The presence of these wobbles has been used in modern times to predict the existence of unseen planets. After Uranus was discovered by William Herschel in 1781, two scientists—Urbain J.J. Leverrier in France and John Couch Adams in England—independently noticed peculiarities in its orbit. These irregularities turned out to be caused by the planet Neptune—first sighted in 1846 by Johann Gottfried Galle. Each time Neptune is close to Uranus it exerts a stronger pull on that planet. When Neptune moves farther away, its attraction to Uranus is weaker. Thus, because of the influence of Neptune, the path that Uranus takes around the Sun is slightly perturbed.

Pluto, discovered in 1930 by Clyde William Tombaugh, was similarly

A Tenth Planet?

Might there be a tenth planet in the Solar System—one that has so far escaped detection? Unlikely. The planetary system around our Sun almost certainly ends with Pluto.

Although there are myriad objects in the Solar System beyond the orbit of Pluto, none qualify as true planets. These far-flung bodies are mainly comets, asteroids and other sorts of debris. They are much too small, and their orbits far too erratic to be considered planets.

Many photographic surveys have been made of the outer Solar System. None has indicated the presence of a tenth planet. And in 1983, an infrared light-detection satellite called the Infrared Astronomy Satellite (IRAS) completed a scan of almost the whole sky and failed to find evidence for such an object. If there is indeed a planet yet to be discovered, it must be either extremely dark, extremely distant, or both.

The ring system of the planet Saturn. Ringed planets in our solar system include Jupiter, Saturn, Uranus, and Neptune.

anticipated because of seeming irregularities in the orbit of Neptune. Though these detected variations turned out to be nothing but observational errors, their apparent existence inspired astronomers to hunt for a ninth planet. With this motivation, Tombaugh searched the sky meticulously and finally found Pluto (which has properties much different than the planet that was predicted from the erroneous data).

There is far more to the Solar System than just the nine planets. Scores of moons (over 60 and still counting) circle these bodies, ranging in diameter from less than ten miles to thousands of miles across. The bulk of these satellites orbit the giant planets: Jupiter, Saturn, Uranus, and Neptune. Earth and Pluto have one moon each, Mars has two, and the rest, none.

The four largest planets also harbor structures known as rings: intricate bands encircling them, composed of billions of chunks of rock and ice. Saturn's ring system has been known since the time of Galileo. The other giant planets' fainter rings were first detected in the late twentieth century.

Between Mars and Jupiter lie the remnants of a planet that never was. Thousands of small stony objects, called *asteroids,* orbit the Sun within this wide belt. These bodies are the remains of a bath of *planetesimals* (the precursors of planets, composed of rock and ice) that once filled the inner Solar System within what is now the orbit of Pluto. Except in the asteroid belt region, most of these planetesimals collided with each other numerous times and eventually coalesced into planets. Therefore, except for a few strays, most of the inner Solar System is free of these bodies. However, close to Jupiter mighty gravitational forces prevented the occurrence of large-scale amalgamation. Instead of merging, the primitive rocks remained as asteroids. The asteroid belt remains today as a fossil of what the entire Solar System once looked like before there were planets.

Besides the zone of asteroids, there is another part of the Solar System where planets never had the chance to form. Far beyond the orbit of Pluto, where the Sun's pull is weakest and temperatures are coldest, reside trillions of icy chunks. (The segment of this region closest to us, named the *Kuiper Belt* for Gerard Kuiper who predicted it 40 years ago,

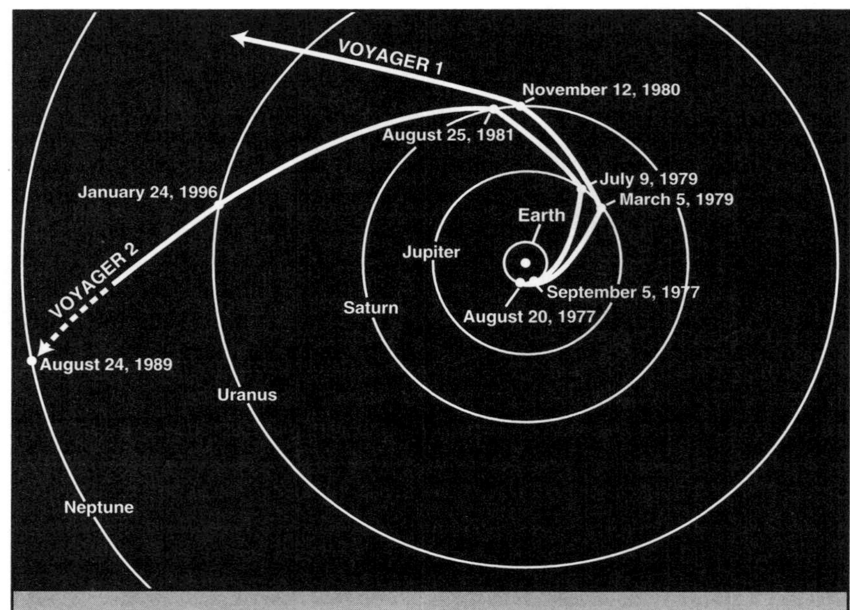

In 1977, Voyagers I and II were launched into space. Each brought back priceless information about the outer reaches of the Solar System, documenting objects, such as moons, that were never before detected.

From *The War of the Worlds*, by H. G. Wells, to *The Martian Chronicles*, pictured here, by Ray Bradbury, science fiction has speculated about life on Mars. No such life forms have been detected. However, in 1996 an asteroid of Martian origin was found to have a fossil record indicating primitive life may have once existed on the red planet.

was first mapped out by the Hubble Space Telescope in 1995.) These scattered fragments comprise planetesimals formed of frozen chemicals. Every once in a while one of these ice-clumps is wrested from its orbit and comes hurling toward the Sun and the inner planets. As it enters this warmer region of space, part of it is vaporized, forming a gaseous tail. The result is the spectacular celestial object known as a comet.

Although the Solar System is the part of the universe that is best known to us, it still contains many mysteries. What is the origin of Pluto, a dwarf planet among giants? Why was it never captured by the gravity of any of the other planets? Why are the rings of Saturn so prominent compared to those of the other large planets? How was the Earth's Moon created? Might there be forms of life on Earth that have come from space? And are there any planets, besides Earth, that contain life or at least the precursors of life? Scientists hope that future manned and unmanned space missions will help us obtain a better understanding of our planetary neighborhood and resolve these and other important questions.

CHAPTER TWO

The Spectacle of Stars

alileo noticed in his observation of the heavens that if he aimed his telescope at a planet, its pointlike shape would appear to grow into a disk. On the other hand, if he fixed it on a star and peered through the scope, the star would still look like a point. This discrepancy, he reasoned, meant that the stars are much farther away than the planets; otherwise, their structure would become apparent under magnification.

Galileo's suspicion that the stars are extremely far away wasn't confirmed until 1838. That year, the German astronomer Friedrich Wilhelm Bessel was the first to measure the distance to a star other than the Sun. Using a method known as *parallax,* he determined the proximity to Earth of the double star system 61 Cygni.

Parallax is a distance-measuring technique that is fairly simple to understand. You can easily try it on your own. Hold one of your fingers about an inch in front of your nose. Observe its position while closing one eye and keeping the other open. Now, note that if you shut the eye that's open and open the eye that's shut, the finger appears to shift position in front of your face. This apparent movement—called parallax—occurs because the angle of observation has changed.

One can readily see how parallax can be used to determine distance. Take the same finger at which you have been staring and position it so that it is now 12 inches in front of your face. Then open and close each of your eyes in succession exactly as you did before. You'll note that the shift due to parallax has become much smaller. As distance to an observed object increases, the amount of displacement due to parallax proportionally decreases.

Jupiter and its satellites.

This principle can be exploited to determine how far away a given object is. First, one calculates how much parallax would be expected for a broad range

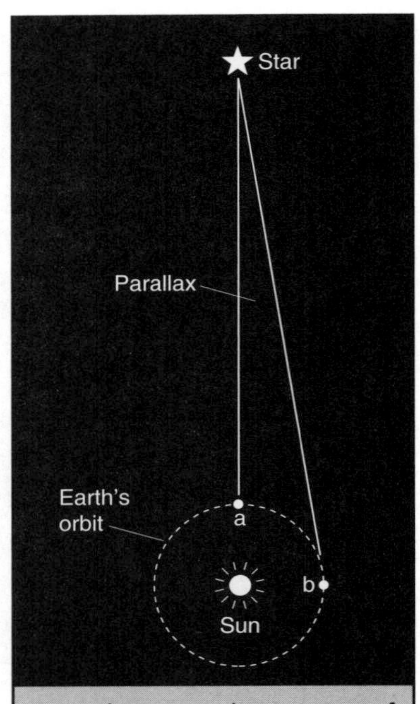

By making two observations of 61 Cygni from opposite parts of the Earth's orbit (a and b), the star's distance from Earth can be measured through the parallax effect.

of distances. Then, by observing the object from two different vantage points, one measures the actual shift that occurs. Finally, one uses the value of this shift to assess the distance to the object.

When Bessel decided to measure the distance to 61 Cygni, he realized that he would need to chose two observation points that were sufficiently distant from each other to obtain significant parallax. He selected as his two points the positions of the Earth during opposite seasons of the year. Between summer and winter, the Earth travels hundreds of millions of miles through space as it orbits around the Sun. This shift in locations creates a parallax effect for many nearby celestial objects.

Bessel turned his telescope to 61 Cygni and noticed that it shifts its angular position in the sky about one five-thousandth of a degree during the course of the year. Making use of his knowledge of parallax, he calculated its distance to be roughly 60 trillion miles away.

In modern astronomical terminology we generally speak of *light-years*, not miles. One light-year, the distance light travels in a year, is about 6 trillion miles. Therefore, we estimate 61 Cygni to be approximately 10 light-years away.

The closest star to Earth, aside from the Sun, is not 61 Cygni but rather a faint red body only 4 light-years away, called Proxima Centauri. Still, in spite of its closeness compared to the other stars, Proxima Centauri is thousands of times more distant from Earth than the farthest objects in the Solar System. If we represent the distance from Earth to

Proxima Centauri by the size of a football field, then the distance from Earth to Pluto would be only the length of a matchstick.

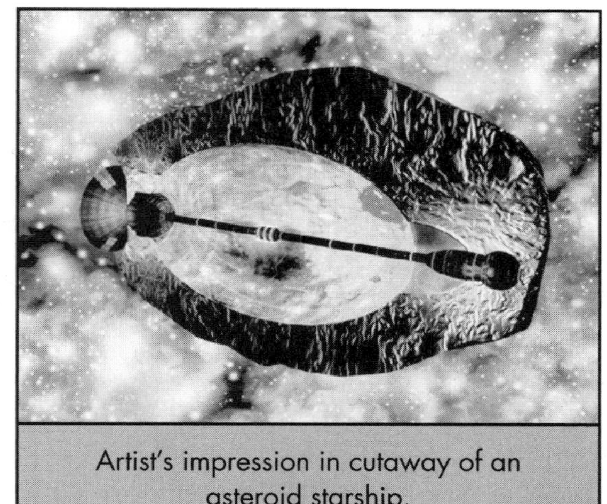

Artist's impression in cutaway of an asteroid starship.

Traveling from Earth to Proxima Centauri would take about a million years at current spaceship speeds. This is obviously far too long for astronauts today to consider such a journey. Perhaps in the future space vessels will be much faster and able to accommodate many generations of families. Only then will interstellar voyages become feasible.

Since the time of Bessel, the distances of millions of stars have been measured and recorded. The overwhelming majority of these measurements, however, have relied on methods other than parallax. The method of parallax has proven to be inadequate for stars more than a few hundred light-years away. Instead, techniques such as the brightness comparison test must be used.

The brightness comparison test relies on the fact that each star has an absolute (also called intrinsic) brightness that represents the actual amount of light that it emits, as well as an apparent brightness that comprises how luminous it appears from Earth. Just as the effectiveness of a light bulb in illuminating a room depends on both its wattage and the size of the room, the apparent brightness of a star depends on both its absolute brightness and its distance. Therefore, if we know both types of brightness for a star we can compute how far away it is.

It seems fairly easy to determine a star's apparent brightness; simply take a reading of how radiant it seems to be. But finding the absolute brightness seems to be a far more difficult task. Clearly, we can't readily travel to a star and measure how much energy it actually puts out. We

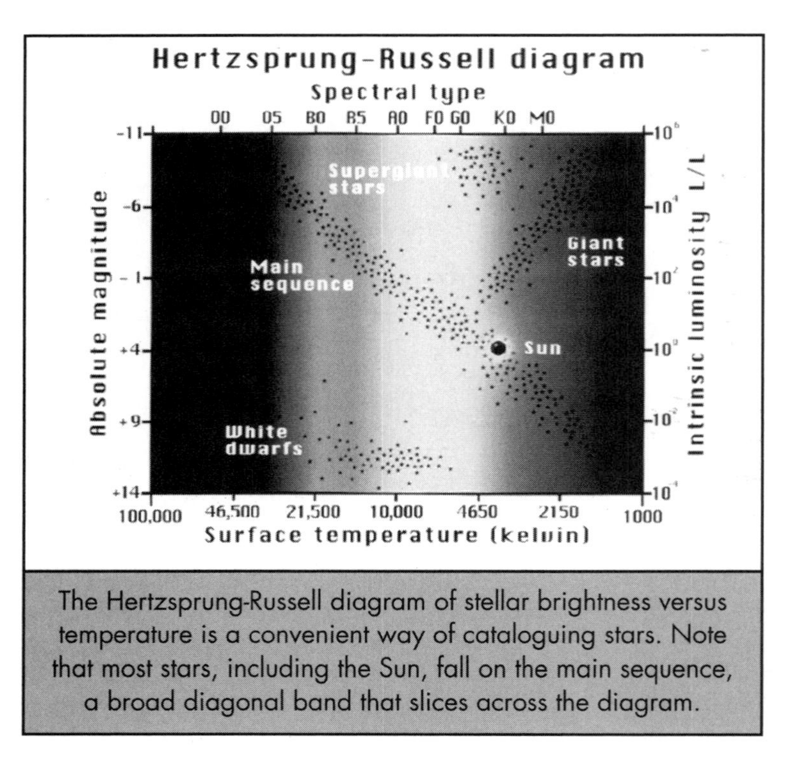

The Hertzsprung-Russell diagram of stellar brightness versus temperature is a convenient way of cataloguing stars. Note that most stars, including the Sun, fall on the main sequence, a broad diagonal band that slices across the diagram.

need to be able to take a reliable guess as to how energetic a star is, without getting close to it.

Fortunately, astronomers have found that for the majority of known stars there is a direct relationship between a star's brilliance and its temperature. Stellar temperatures are straightforward to measure; they are indicated by stars' colors. For example, blue is hotter than orange, and orange is hotter than red. In most cases, one can use this information to determine how much light a given star emits. If one plots the temperatures of stars versus their absolute brightness, on a graph called an H-R (Herzsprung-Russell) diagram, most stars fall along a band called the *main sequence.* Along the main sequence, the hotter the star, the greater its brilliance. Therefore, main sequence stars that are blue tend to give off more light than those that are yellow. Those that shine yellow, in turn, are intrinsically brighter than orange stars, and those that are orange are brighter than red

Stellar Oddities

Most stars live along the main sequence, a zone in which temperature and brightness are closely related. Main sequence stars shine at a constant rate, more or less. Yet for every rule there are exceptions. Red giants, the colossus of stars, burn out quickly, expelling energy in rapid pace through their large surface areas. White dwarfs, on the other hand, glow white-hot and dim, cooling down slowly like glowing embers at a campfire.

But even stranger stars lurk in the heavens. A class of giant yellow stars known as Cepheids vary periodically in size and brightness. They rhythmically expand and contract, pulsating in and out like bellows. As they contract, they release energy in bursts. Astronomers have discovered that the rate of these emissions depends entirely on the variable star's absolute brightness. In other words, the period of a Cepheid (a quantity easily measured) is proportional to its brilliance. Because knowledge of a celestial body's absolute brightness is tantamount to knowing how far away it is, Cepheids make excellent distance indicators.

stars. The Sun is an excellent example of a main sequence star; its temperature and brightness fall within the range appropriate for this grouping.

If astronomers determine that a star falls within the main sequence, then they can readily estimate its distance. First, they assess the star's apparent brightness by recording (for a given time interval) how much of the star's light arrives on Earth. Then, they measure its temperature through a careful determination of its color. This is normally done by use of a spectroscope—a device that can evaluate the entire range of light frequencies put out by a star. Next, they compare the star on an H-R diagram to other main sequence stars of the same temperature. They use this comparison to find the star's expected absolute brightness. Finally, they determine the ratio between the star's apparent brightness and its absolute brightness. The smaller this ratio, the farther away the star is from Earth.

Not all stars fall along the main sequence. Some stars, called *red giants,* are red, but large and luminous. Though they shine brightly, they have extremely low surface temperatures. Other stars, called *white dwarfs,* are tiny, dim, and white-hot. These notable exceptions are believed to be former main sequence stars near the ends of their life cycles.

Unlike bodies that give off energy at a constant rate—light bulbs, for example—stars burn with greater or lesser intensity during different stages of their lives. Eventually, all stars burn out, but not before putting on spectacular light shows in the process.

Until the early-to-mid twentieth century, scientists believed that stars generate energy by shrinking. As they contracted, it was thought, they would get hotter and hotter, giving off light in the process. This could not be the primary way that stars shine, however. If it were, they would scarcely last a million years, rather than the billions of years of age that we know them to have.

Now we know that stars are fueled by nuclear fusion, the process of building heavier elements from lighter components. Each time fusion takes place, energy is released as a by-product. This energy, expelled into space, is what we see as starlight.

The fusion process begins when the nuclei (or cores) of two hydrogen atoms smash together to form a particle called the deuteron. A deuteron, the nucleus of deuterium (heavy hydrogen), is a combination of a positive proton and a neutral neutron. Deuterons readily combine with additional protons to form helium. Helium, in turn, can fuse together to form heavier elements, such as carbon. In a typical star, merger after merger takes place until significant quantities of higher elements are built up.

We must distinguish, at this point, between two different stellar types: Population I and Population II. These groups are characterized by their relative ages, the latter being much older than the former. They can also be distinguished by their locations. Our galaxy, the Milky Way, is shaped like a flying saucer—a flat disk surrounding a central bulge. Whereas Population I stars are found mainly in the galactic disk, Population II stars mostly reside in the central bulge of the galaxy and in the halo surrounding this bulge.

Population II stars date back to the early stages of the universe. Formed at a time when the cosmos was filled with hydrogen and helium gases, they contain practically no heavy elements. Their fires are lit by nuclear fusion of light nuclei, such as those of hydrogen and deuterium. They shine until their fusible material is exhausted.

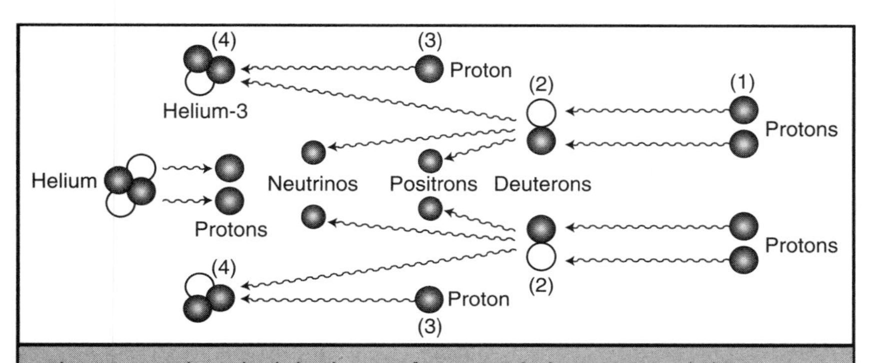

The process by which hydrogen fuses into helium proceeds by stages. First, protons (1) combine to form deuterons (2). Then, deuterons unite with protons (3) to form helium-3 (4) (a helium isotope). Finally, helium-3 nuclei merge to yield ordinary helium. Energy is released in every step.

When Population II stars die, their material is spread out into space. Some of this dust is eventually incorporated into newly formed Population I stars. In this manner is the substance of the cosmos recycled.

Though Population I stars consist mostly of hydrogen and helium gas, they also contain heavy elements (heavier than helium), which comprise about 1 or 2 percent of their mass. These heavier materials are fused from the lighter elements that the stars have collected. The Sun is a good example of a Population I star. It contains material that once belonged to stars from previous generations.

What will happen when the Sun itself dies? In several billion years our mother star will burn much brighter. It will expend more and more of its nuclear fuel, until little is left of its original hydrogen. Then, at some point in the far future, all nuclear reactions in the Sun's center will cease.

Once the Sun passes into its "postnuclear" phase, it will separate effectively into two different regions: an inner zone and an outer zone. These sectors are distinguished by the fact that while no more hydrogen fuel will remain in the inner zone, there will be a small amount left in the outer zone. Rapidly, changes will begin to take place that will serve to tear the Sun apart. The inner zone, its nuclear fires no longer burning, will begin to collapse under the influence of its own weight. It will contract into a tiny hot core, dense and dim.

The Solar Neutrino Dilemma

One of the results of nuclear fusion, the process that causes stars to shine, is the production of tiny subatomic particles called neutrinos. The Sun, for example, creates *neutrinos* each time its constituent hydrogen atoms fuse into helium. So, one way to prove that fusion occurs in the Sun would be to count the number of neutrinos given off.

Neutrinos are notoriously slippery creatures, extremely difficult to catch. They interact so rarely with other particles that it would take a light-year of lead to stop a single one. Nevertheless, human persistence being what it is, a method has been developed to trap these elusive objects. For twenty years, an experiment has been running deep in the Homestake gold mine in South Dakota to detect solar neutrinos in a hundred thousand gallon vat of a chlorine-based cleaning fluid. It relies upon the fact that so many neutrinos are given off by the Sun, some are bound to interact.

As solar neutrinos hit the liquid, they turn some of the chlorine into radioactive argon. The amount of argon produced tells scientists how many neutrinos are emitted. Then, this quantity is compared to theoretical predictions.

For a long time, however, theory came up short. Solar fusion models were predicting far more neutrinos than were actually observed. Given the long-held assumption that neutrinos have zero mass—and hence cannot decay into other particles—researchers simply couldn't explain the fact that only about a quarter of the solar neutrinos expected were actually detected.

Recently, though, a team of physicists at Los Alamos Laboratory have experimentally determined that the neutrino has a small, but nonzero, mass. If accurate, this finding would explain the former discrepancy between theoretical and measured neutrino counts; apparently, many of the neutrinos produced by the Sun decayed before reaching the detector. A long-standing puzzle seems to have been solved.

Billions of years from now the Sun will swell up and become a red giant star.

An opposite fate will await the outer region, a loosely held together ball of gas. A shock wave caused by the inner zone's contraction will send ripples through the dying star, pushing the stellar exterior's material farther and farther outward. The outer envelope will then grow rapidly, increasing, in a short interval, hundreds of times in size. As it expands, it will cool down, lowering in temperature by thousands of degrees.

Eventually, the Sun will become a red giant star, cool and bright. It will be so large that it will occupy the whole space that used to be the Earth's orbit, and so brilliant that it will be able to be seen with the naked eye thousands of light-years away. It will exist that way for millions of years, gradually releasing the material of its outer envelope into space.

Finally, nothing will be left of the gaseous exterior of the Sun. All that remains will be the hot, white core. The Sun will have become a white dwarf star. The core will shrink, giving off the last of its energy, and the Sun will finally die.

CHAPTER THREE

Puzzling Pulsars

Stars of less than a few times the Sun's mass share its fate; they eventually become white dwarfs and fade into extinction. Along the way, they pass through the same stages the Sun goes through (though at different rates, depending on how heavy they are).

Massive stellar bodies, however, undergo a much more dramatic type of evolution. They meet their ends in powerful supernova explosions, emitting, for a time, more light than the rest of the stars in the galaxy put together.

In 1987, the world witnessed an unexpected display of celestial fireworks—a modern supernova explosion. The first person to see the flash was a technician, Oscar Duhalde, at the Las Campanas Observatory in Chile. During a coffee break in the early morning hours of February 24, he noticed that a region of the sky near a gaseous formation called the Tarantula Nebula was especially bright. But he didn't think much of it until he met several hours later with his colleague, the Canadian astronomer Ian Shelton.

That morning, Shelton, who had dropped out of graduate school to take a full-time job as the resident observer of the University of Toronto's Southern Observatory at Las Campanas, was taking a routine survey of the Large Magellanic Cloud (a small satellite galaxy of the Milky Way). To do this, he exposed a photographic plate to the light coming from a wide-view telescope, called an astrograph. When he later developed the plate he found a huge bright spot that shouldn't have been there at all.

Shelton was astounded. Either there was a flaw in the equipment, or something new was out there. He stepped outside and looked up at the predawn sky. Sure enough, smack in the middle of the region of the sky that contains the Large Magellanic Cloud was a bright new star, where none had been before.

Convinced that he had made a major discovery, Shelton walked over

The supernova of 1987, sometimes called Supernova Shelton-Duhalde-Jones, was a cataclysmic event witnessed around the world.

to the facility where Duhalde and several others were working. Shelton and Duhalde shared their experiences and decided that they had seen a *supernova*—an exploding star hundreds of thousands of light-years away. Duhalde and a colleague quickly dispatched a telegram to the Central Bureau for Astronomical Telegrams in Massachusetts, a clearinghouse for astronomical findings.

Shortly after the group in Chile recorded their observations, an amateur astronomer in New Zealand, Albert Jones, independently reported his own sighting of the supernova. For this reason, the 1987 event is sometimes called Supernova Shelton-Duhalde-Jones. More commonly it is known as Supernova 1987A.

Supernova explosions occur as part of the end stage of the life of extremely massive stars, called supergiants. (We speak here of one familiar class of supernova, called Type II.) In some respects, these stellar titans

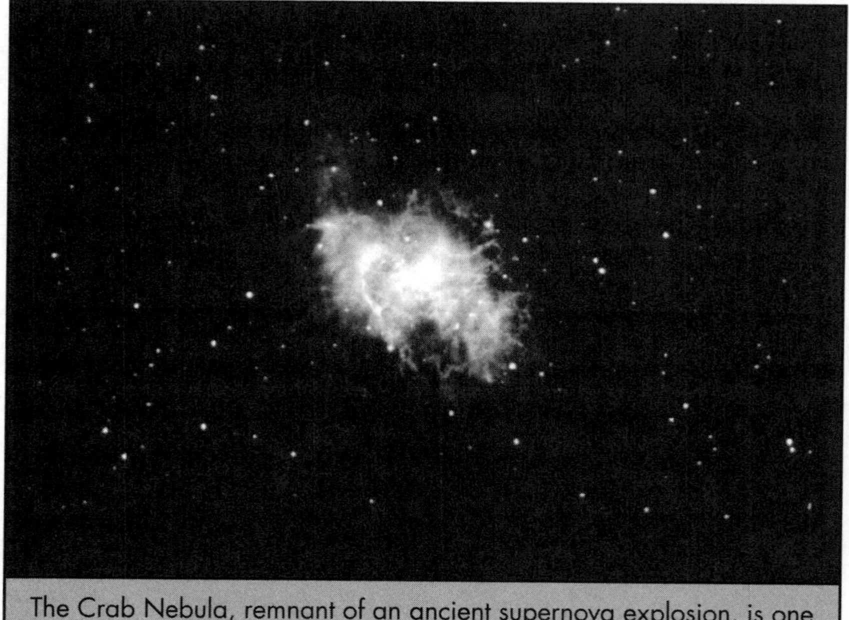

The Crab Nebula, remnant of an ancient supernova explosion, is one of the most colorful sights in the galaxy.

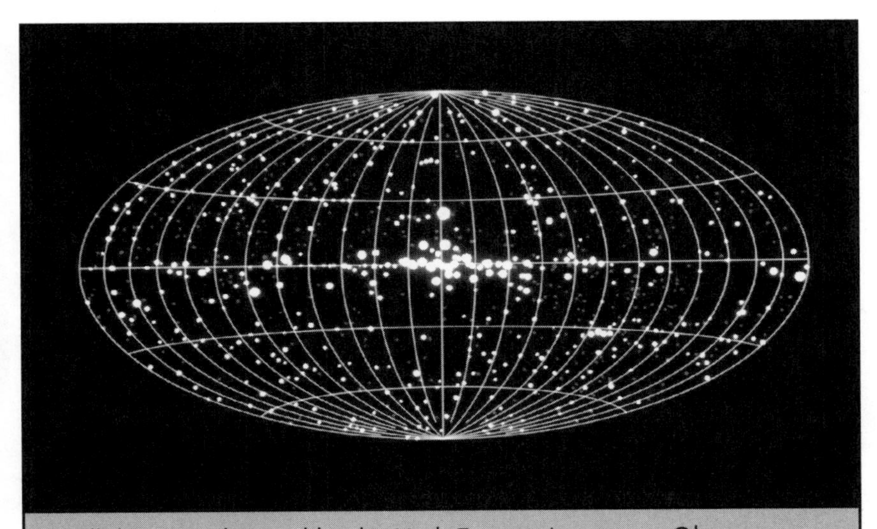

All-sky map obtained by the High Energy Astronomy Observatory satellite (HEAO-1). The clusters of large circles at the center are binary star systems in which a neutron star accretes matter. Neutron stars are formed from the collapsed cores of massive stars.

resemble ordinary giants; both have fiery compact cores surrounded by cooler gaseous envelopes. The difference between the two lies in their ultimate evolutionary paths. The centers of giants are just about hot enough to ignite the nuclear fusion to produce only a few types of heavy elements. Eventually, the process stops, and a white dwarf is left.

In contrast, the cores of supergiants are far denser and therefore much hotter. They serve as cauldrons to fuse together lighter atoms and forge numerous heavy elements. Gradually, more and more complex materials are built up—from carbon to magnesium to silicon and sulfur and eventually to iron.

Once iron is produced in its core, the supergiant has reached the end of the line. Iron cannot fuse together on its own to form more heavier elements. Therefore, in the absence of the possibility of greater fusion, the only way the core can gain more energy is simply to collapse. And collapse it does. Within a tenth of a second, the core contracts down to a sphere less than seventy miles across.

This catastrophic collapse releases incredible amounts of energy, enough to blast the rest of the star millions of miles through space. The gas that is blown off in this shock wave sometimes settles into a wispy, colorful formation known as a *supernova remnant.* The Crab Nebula is an outstanding example of such a relic.

A supernova explosion is sudden, no doubt. In the blink of an eye, a supergiant—one of the largest stars in the sky—completely disinte-

A pulsar acts as a celestial lighthouse beacon, rotating rapidly and giving off a pulsating signal.

Gamma Ray Bursts

One of the longest-standing mysteries in astronomy is the origin of the intense blasts of high energy, called *gamma ray bursts.* Gamma ray bursts were first discovered in the 1960s by the U.S. military, when they were spotted during satellite surveys intended to monitor nuclear explosions. These streams of radiation appear to come from all parts of the sky—with one burst, on average, appearing every day. Since 1973, information about these anomalies has been declassified, and theorists have been busy trying to solve a rather difficult puzzle: what creates such frequent and powerful explosions?

A number of researchers, including Tsvi Piran of Hebrew University in Jerusalem, have speculated that gamma ray bursts are the products of neutron star collisions. In Piran's model, two neutron stars start out as part of a binary system, circling one another. Eventually, the pair becomes unstable, and the compact bodies crash into one another. This creates a torrent of particle formation, presenting itself in the form of high-frequency gamma radiation. Others theorize that the blasts occur when matter from neighboring stars is injected into neutron stars at extremely high speeds. This would also create a flood of radiation. Astronomers hope to test these hypotheses by carefully observing the vicinities of detected neutron stars.

grates. Of the original stellar mass, only the contracted core remains: an ultradense object known as a *neutron star.* It has been given that name because it is purely composed of neutrons (the protons and electrons have been squeezed together).

Neutron stars have been detected by astronomers by means of their intense radiation, usually present in the form of radio waves. The first sighting of such an object was in 1967, when Jocelyn Bell and Anthony

Planets Around Pulsars

In the early 1990s, Alex Wolszczan of Pennsylvania State University, along with colleague Dale Frail of the National Radio Astronomy Observatory, made a phenomenal discovery about pulsars. While performing a sky scan with the 305-meter-diameter radio telescope at the Arecido Observatory in Puerto Rico, they turned up evidence of an entire planetary system circling a pulsar called PSR 1257 + 12. Signs of planets showed up as deviations in the pulsar's signals caused by gravitational tugs on the pulsar by unseen objects.

Not only are the planets around 1257 + 12 the first such objects discovered near pulsars, they are also the first planetary bodies found outside the Solar System. (Other planets, circling ordinary stars, have been subsequently found.) Theorists believe that they were created from the material captured by the neutron star from the destruction of a stellar companion.

Hewish noticed regular variations in radio wave signals from a source in a constellation they were observing. At first, they thought that these periodic pulses might be messages sent from extraterrestrial civilizations. They wondered if an advanced society located on a distant alien planet could possibly be sending greetings to Earth.

Soon they realized the true source of the signals: a neutron star of approximately 6 miles in diameter. They estimated this body to be spinning once every one and one-third seconds, fast enough to produce the pulses observed. Because of its rapid production of regular signals, they called this object a *pulsar.*

Today the terms "neutron star" and "pulsar" are used more or less

The pulsar 1257 + 12 (center) as seen from its innermost planet (bottom).

interchangeably. Typically, the former term is used for theoretical discussions, especially about the object's composition, and the latter for physical descriptions, particularly of the body's rotational properties.

Why do pulsars spin so rapidly? The answer lies in a physical principle called *conservation of angular momentum.* Angular momentum is a property of an object that depends on three factors: its mass, its spread, and how fast it is spinning. It is a constant in nature, which means that for a solitary body, it cannot be created or destroyed. Therefore, assuming that a rotating object maintains a constant mass, it must spin slower if it spreads out and faster if it draws itself inward. The same principle is the reason that ice skaters spin much more rapidly when they pull their arms in toward their bodies.

Ballet dancers pull their arms in to spin more rapidly. The reason is that angular momentum—the product of rotational speed, mass, and outward extension—is always conserved.

Applying the law of angular momentum conservation to pulsars, we can see why they spin so quickly. As the stellar core of the star that produced the pulsar shrinks down, it must spin faster and faster to keep the total angular momentum constant. Therefore, a pulsar rotates with such great speed because its collapse has been so profound.

Shortly after the discovery by Bell and Hewish, a pulsar was detected in the Crab Nebula. Astronomers had been certain for years that the Crab Nebula was the remnant of a supernova. Therefore, the fact that a pulsar was found at that site confirmed their theories that neutron stars are produced in such explosions.

Hundreds of pulsars have been observed in our galaxy since the time of Bell and Hewish's discovery. Undoubtedly, many more remain to be found. Some scientists, such as Thomas Tauris of Aarhus University in Denmark, theorize that there are hundreds of thousands of pulsars in the Milky Way too dim to be easily seen.

Tauris bases this speculation on his own discovery of a faint pulsar, called PSR J0108–1431, located only 280 light-years away in the constellation Cetus. In 1994, he found this object, which spins 74 times a minute, using the radio telescope in Parkes, Australia. It has proven to be the closest, dimmest pulsar ever detected.

CHAPTER FOUR

The Lair of Black Holes

In many communities there are one or two enigmatic individuals who let little be known about themselves. These recluses live their lives stealthily, hoping that others will simply leave them alone and not ask too many probing questions.

There are such reclusive characters in the cosmos as well. *Black holes,* the ultradense end-products of the most massive stars in space, are the mysterious hermits of the universe. Shielded in cloaks of secrecy, they allow virtually no information about themselves to leak out.

The term "black hole" itself was coined by Princeton physicist John Wheeler in 1968 in an article entitled "Our universe, the known and unknown." Wheeler was tired of using the expression "gravitationally collapsed object" and wanted to create a term of greater simplicity and with better descriptive power. He thought "black hole" sounded much more evocative.

John Wheeler, the American astrophysicist who coined the term "black hole," receiving the Enrico Fermi award from President Lyndon B. Johnson in 1968.

A black hole is created during the collapse of an especially massive supergiant. During this process, as in neutron star creation, the iron core in the star's center contracts very quickly under its own weight, giving off a powerful blast of energy. In the case of neutron stars, however, this collapse halts as soon as

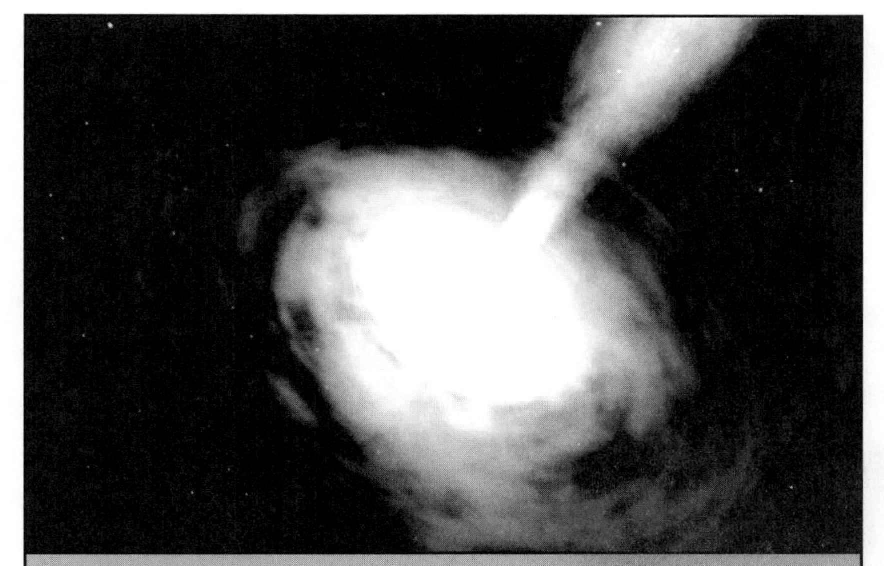

Artist's impression of a black hole. Black holes, the final states of very massive stars, are created through gravitational self-attraction. In reality, no light escapes from a black hole.

all of the matter in the core has turned into neutrons and been compressed into a tight ball. In contrast, black holes are born when the mass of the core is so great that the collapse continues indefinitely. The neutrons themselves are pulverized under the crushing force of gravitational self-attraction. What is left is a material of unimaginably high density.

Because black holes are so massive, they harbor immense gravitational fields. These forces are so powerful that nothing can escape them, not even light. That is why these objects are called "black"; they allow nothing from inside their boundaries to be seen.

To understand the dynamics of black holes, and to fathom how they prevent all things from escaping from their interiors, we need to discuss *general relativity.* General relativity is Einstein's successful theory of gravity that pertains to planets, stars, and black holes alike. Proposed by Einstein in 1916, it describes how space and time (in combination, called

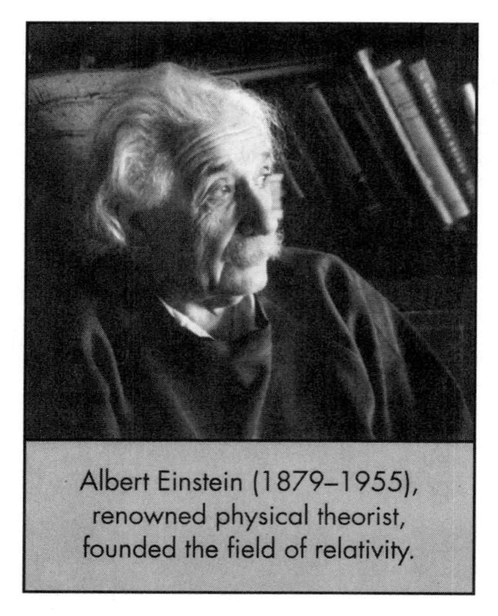

Albert Einstein (1879–1955), renowned physical theorist, founded the field of relativity.

space-time) are distorted by the presence of massive bodies. In short, it states that matter bends space, and that the bending of space, in turn, affects the motion of objects traveling through it. (The popular term "space warp"—omnipresent in science fiction books and movies—is an expression of this principle.)

Let us visualize how Einstein's model works. First, let's think of time as the fourth dimension of reality—along with the three spatial dimensions, length, width, and height. (It's hard to picture a direction other than the ordinary three, but let's try our best.) Second, let's consider space-time to be the surface of a giant trampoline, stretched out tight.

Now, Einstein's theory states that mass curves space-time. We represent this by placing a stone on the surface of the trampoline. The weight of the stone causes the stretchy material to droop downward a little bit. Though the trampoline is still mainly flat, it now has a slight dent in the middle.

We now place several stones on the trampoline. These have an even greater effect, causing the surface to positively sag. In fact, the more stones, the more curved the trampoline becomes.

In this manner, massive bodies in the universe cause the cosmic fabric to become distorted. Just as ten stones bend a trampoline's surface much more than one does, objects of much greater mass than the Sun curve space far more than those of one solar mass or less.

If a tennis ball is rolled across the top of a flat, fully stretched trampoline, it follows a straight line. In contrast, if it is sent whirling across one that has a indentation, it engages in a curved path. Similarly, objects traveling through flat regions of space-time (with little heavy matter) continue along straight-line paths, and those traveling through curved

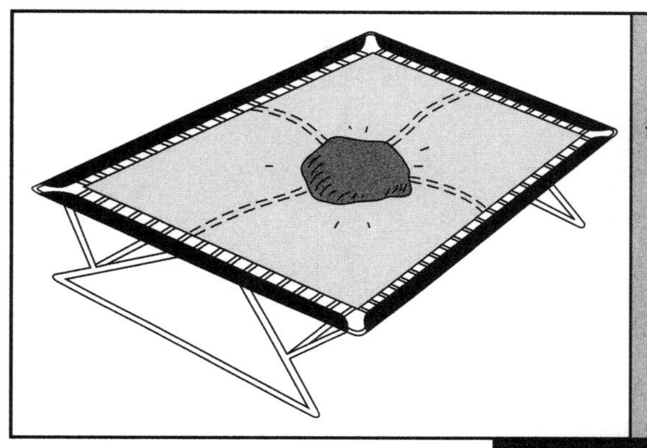

Stones resting on a trampoline distort the trampoline's shape. Similarly, in general relativity, massive objects curve the structure of space-time. A black hole is so dense that it creates a rip in the surface of space-time.

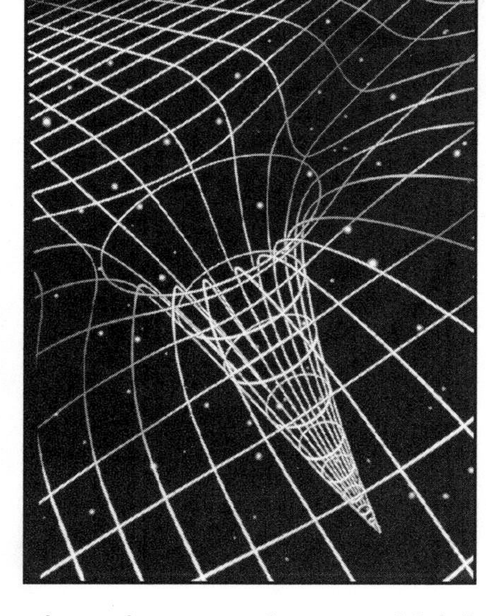

regions (with much heavy matter) move in curved trajectories.

To complete our analogy, we now examine the effects of black holes on their surrounding space-time regions. We represent these ultradense objects by the placement of an extremely massive boulder on the trampoline. Naturally, this would affect the mat considerably. Not only would its surface bend, it would likely break. In similar manner, the existence of a black hole in a region of the cosmos would serve to rip its very fabric apart. This tear in the structure of space-time is called a *singularity.*

Now we can see why nothing can escape from a black hole. Just as a tennis ball, rolled over the surface of a trampoline, would fall through the hole created by a boulder, an object moving through the space near a black hole would become captured by its steep gravitational well. Moreover, in the case of a black hole, it would take an infinite amount of energy to retrieve the unfortunate body.

Black Holes as Time Tunnels?

We have seen that a black hole distorts spatial paths in its vicinity. According to Einstein's dictum that space and time are interwoven, it follows that time is also warped near such an object. For this reason, some researchers have suggested using black holes as time machines.

Indeed, if an astronaut were to place a large clock aboard her spaceship before setting sail for a black hole, an outside observer (in a space station nearby, let's say) would perceive the clock to be slowing down as the astronaut approached the collapsed star's perimeter. To the onlooker, she would seem to move slower and slower as well; she would never appear to reach the event horizon border. Finally, she would look frozen in time—stunned, like a deer blinded by headlights.

From the astronaut's point of view, these events would take place quite differently. The clock on board the ship would tick on at its usual rate. Thus, no reprieve would be granted for the astronaut from her rapid plunge into the dark abyss. She wouldn't even notice the moment when she passed through the event horizon, but, nevertheless, she would become stuck in the black hole from that point on.

Suppose, however, as she descended, she were to observe the region of space above her. Looking outside the ship, the hapless passenger would see everything speed up in time. The whole of future history would pass before her eyes in a flash. But this sort of time travel would be pointless. She wouldn't be able to interact with the rest of the universe; instead, she'd be doomed to perish (unless she could turn her

How close can you come to a black hole without being snatched in forever? Pretty close, it turns out. The point of no return is known as the *event horizon,* a spherical shell located a distance from the black hole's center called the *Schwarzschild radius.* This radius depends solely on the mass of the black hole. A black hole of solar mass, for instance, would have a Schwarzschild radius of less than 2 miles. Therefore, you could venture no closer than 2 miles from its center, or you'd surely be gone for good.

Clocks approaching the event horizon of a black hole would appear to an outside observer to slow down. As they neared the event horizon, their ticks would become more and more spaced out. Their last tick, infinitely long, would take place just as the clocks reached the event horizon.

ship around in time). So, in summary, although an astronaut might experience a type of time travel near the event horizon of a black hole, it would likely be a fatal—and therefore pointless—expedition.

Once you were within the event horizon, there would be no turning back. You would be drawn downward toward the dead center of the hole where the space-time singularity lies. Within a fraction of a second, you'd be pulverized by the infinitely large gravitational forces present there.

We have said that nothing that goes into a black hole can ever leave it. Yet scientists have come to realize that black holes slowly give off energy. How can this be? Renowned British physicist Stephen Hawking

Stephen Hawking, British cosmologist.

showed in 1974 that black holes have a nonzero temperature, somewhat higher than that of deep space. All objects that are warmer than their surroundings must expel heat—and black holes are no exception. It would take, however, billions and billions of years for a typical black hole to evaporate completely (give off all its energy) in this manner. The energy given off by a black hole is called, appropriately enough, *Hawking radiation.*

The term "black hole" is one of the astronomical expressions most familiar to the general public. One would assume from this familiarity that their actuality is beyond dispute. For a long time, though, black holes were considered merely hypothetical objects. Viewed as mathematical constructs, they were seen as little more than the subject of clever exercises for graduate students.

In recent years, however, there has been a growing body of evidence that black holes exist in space. This proof hasn't come directly—black holes are invisible, after all—but rather through the radiation emitted by matter falling into event horizons. Detecting black holes by this method is like finding burnt coal in a campfire by observing shadows in the flames.

In the summer of 1994, strong evidence was found by the Hubble Space Telescope for a supermassive black hole in the center of M87, a galaxy in the Virgo Cluster 50 million light-years away. Images taken by the telescope's wide-field camera indicated the presence there of large quantities of glowing interstellar gas moving at phenomenal speeds. These large velocities were likely produced by a compact object of 2 billion solar masses, confined to a region of less than a few hundred billion miles

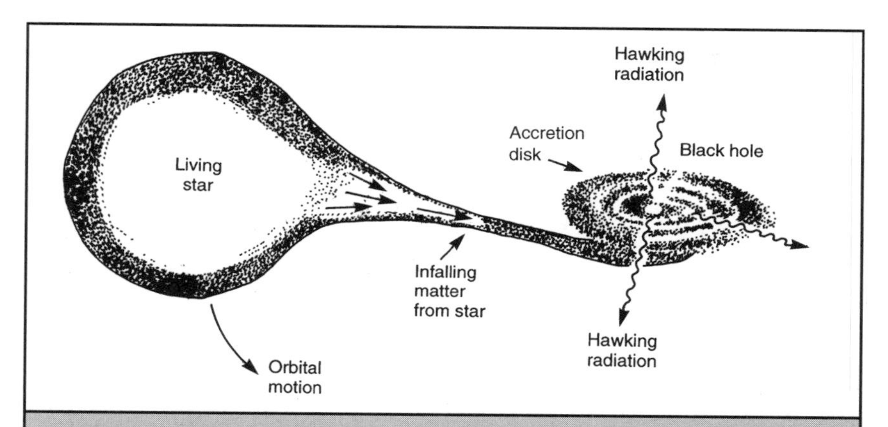

If a living star is unlucky enough to have a black hole companion, the star's material is continuously drawn away. This matter gives off luminous energy as it falls into the black hole's center.

across. This immense density strongly points to the existence of a supermassive black hole in the core of M87.

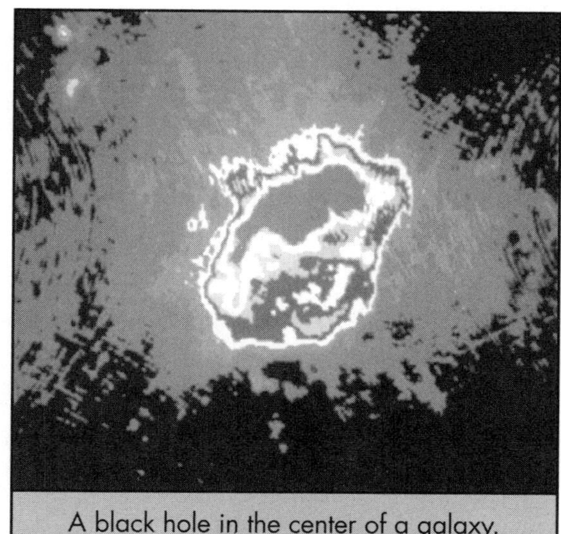

A black hole in the center of a galaxy.

Many theorists are convinced that a supermassive black hole lies in the middle of our own galaxy as well. So far, positive proof of this has yet to be found. Scientists hope that future searches with the Hubble Space Telescope will help to resolve this fascinating question.

CHAPTER FIVE

Galactic Rhythms

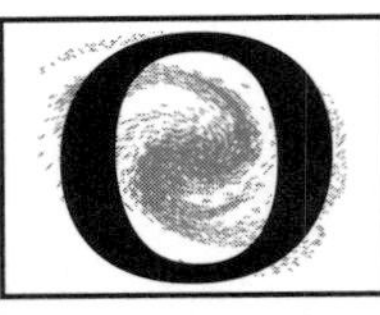

bjects such as M87, where the Hubble Telescope recently found evidence for a black hole, are millions of light-years away from Earth. They lie far outside the perimeter of the Milky Way and therefore do not belong to it. Rather, they are independent galaxies in their own right.

Interestingly, it is only in modern times that astronomers have known that other galaxies exist beyond ours. For many years they believed that (what we now know to be) galaxies were gaseous clouds, called nebulae, located well within the confines of the Milky Way. Using a telescope, these nebulae can be seen scattered throughout the sky as hazy formations of various shapes and sizes.

It wasn't until the 1920s that young astronomer Edwin Hubble measured the distances to these "nebulae" and proved that they could not lie inside our own galactic domain. Hubble, during the period between the two World Wars, used the Hooker telescope at Mount Wilson to locate and map out many of these objects. To calculate how far away from us they are, he used a method known as the Cepheid variable technique.

Cepheid stars have the property—desirable in the field of astronomical measurement—that their light output periodically increases and decreases at a rate that depends on their absolute brightness. By measuring this period, one can determine a Cepheid's absolute brightness. Then, one can match the Cepheid's absolute brightness to its apparent brightness and thereby figure out how far away it is. For this reason, Cepheids are known as "standard candles"; their predictable light output makes them outstanding distance indicators.

By analogy, one might imagine standing at one end of a long, drafty hallway lined with flickering torches—with each torch putting out the same amount of light. Suddenly, each of the torches, except one, is extin-

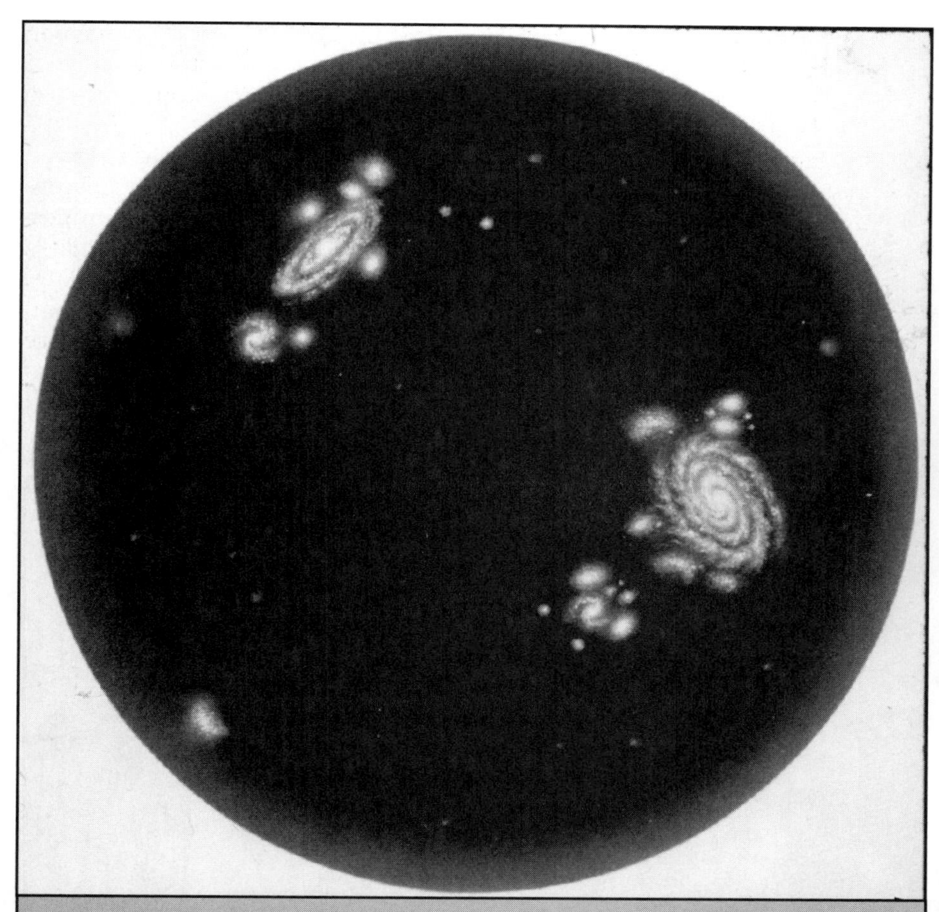

Artist's rendition of some of the members of the Local Group, the cluster of galaxies to which the Milky Way belongs.

guished by a blast of wind. By comparing the brightness of the remaining flame to the standard brightness of torches, one can calculate the distance of the torch that is still burning. In a similar manner, astronomers use Cepheids' brightnesses to determine their distances.

Hubble applied the Cepheid variable method to the spiral-shaped body that was then known as the Andromeda Nebula. In 1924 he discovered a dozen Cepheids in Andromeda and used their variational properties to measure the distance to them. His result was that Andromeda is approximately 1 million light-years away, a figure about 10 times greater than the diameter of the Milky Way. Thus, Hubble proved that Andromeda must be much farther away—and therefore much larger—than once thought. Reassessing its size, he calculated it to be of galactic dimensions. Today, thanks to Hubble, we consider Andromeda to be the closest galaxy to our own that resembles the Milky Way in size and appearance.

Edwin Hubble, pioneering astronomer who discovered the expansion of the universe.

The Hooker telescope at Mount Wilson Observatory near Los Angeles.

There are other galaxies—smaller ones—that are even closer to us than Andromeda. For a long time it was believed that two structures called the Magellanic Clouds were the nearest "island universes" to our own. The Large Magellanic Cloud, the closer of the two, is a petite irregular galaxy over 170,000 light-years from the Milky Way. It and the Small Magellanic Cloud are satellites of ours, gravitationally bound to the Milky Way like dogs on a leash.

In 1994, astronomers Rodrigo Ibata, Mike Irwin, and Gerry Gilmore of the University of Cambridge, working at the Schmidt Telescope in Australia, announced the discovery of a galaxy even closer than the Magellanic Clouds. Named the Sagittarius dwarf, it is just 50,000 light-years from the center of our own galaxy. It is so close that it is destined

Andromeda, the closest spiral galaxy to our own.

to fall into and then become cannibalized by the Milky Way within a period of a few hundred million years.

Why wasn't this nearby system discovered earlier? The reason is clear: the Sagittarius dwarf is located on the other side of the central bulge of our galaxy. Within this bulge resides an enormous amount of extremely massive stars, shrouded in a thick haze of interstellar dust and gases. It is no wonder that little can be seen beyond this crowded domain.

To spot the new galaxy, the scientists employed a device called a multiple-optical-fiber spectrograph. This instrument ascertains the radial velocities (speed away from Earth) of distant stars by measuring the shifting frequencies of the light that they produce. (It relies on the Doppler effect, a relationship between frequency and velocity to be discussed in Chapter Six.)

The Cambridge team used this device to determine the speeds of over a million stars in the Milky Way's bulge. Of these stars, a group of about a hundred seemed to be moving in unison. Moreover, this same group appeared to share the same basic composition. The astronomers concluded from this data that they didn't belong to the Milky Way at all, but rather to a new galaxy—the Sagittarius dwarf.

We have mentioned so far several different types of galaxies: spirals, irregulars, and dwarfs. The first two categories are shape descriptors; the third refers to size. Thus, there can be dwarf spirals and dwarf irregulars, as well as giant spirals and giant irregulars.

Spirals are characterized by a thick central bulge surrounded by a pinwheel-shaped disk. They contain stars of all ages—juvenile Population I stars and elderly Population II stars. Andromeda is a superb example of this type of galaxy.

Irregulars, on the other hand, such as the Small and Large Magellanic Clouds, possess distorted appearances. In many cases, they are stretched out and otherwise misshapen by the gravitational pull of neighboring galaxies. This is certainly what is happening to the Magellanic Clouds; they are literally being torn apart by the forces exerted by the Milky Way.

Other galactic shape categories include elliptical and barred spirals. Elliptical, the most common type of galaxy, look like ovals rotated about their axes—galactic footballs, in other words. Because they have few gas reserves for new stars to form, they contain almost exclusively older, Population II stars. Typically, elliptical galaxies are fairly small; most are dwarfs.

Barred spirals, the rarest of the regular galaxy types, are distinguished from normal spirals by the presence of a bright central bar that connects the spiral arms. It is not yet completely understood why this bar exists.

Traditionally, the Milky Way has been pictured as an ordinary spiral.

Galaxies distributed in space. They can be (a) elliptical, (b) spiral, (c) barred spiral, or irregular.

(a)

(b)

(c)

(a)

(b)

(c)

The Shape of the Milky Way

We live in the outer reaches of one of the spiral arms of the Milky Way. Because astronomers cannot step beyond this vantage point and look at our galaxy from above, they can only take an educated guess as to what it looks like in its entirety. Telescopic observations over the past century have led the scientific community to conclude that the shape of the Milky Way is similar to that of a pinwheel.

In 1995, however, this long-held belief—almost a truism—was put to the test. A new type of analysis being employed to map out the galaxy, called *gravitational microlensing,* yielded its first comprehensive results. Instead of the expected simple yolklike nucleus, the Milky Way was found by a team of American, British, and Australian researchers to have a bar in its center.

Gravitational microlensing relies on the general relativistic fact that the presence of matter curves space and hence affects the path taken by light. In this manner, massive objects act as giant lenses, curving and focusing incoming rays and creating distorted images of distant objects.

In this case, the light given off by the Large Magellanic Cloud was bent on the way to reaching us by the presence of intermediate stars. Stellar material in our own galaxy curved this light's path and altered slightly the way the Large Magellanic Cloud appeared. This effect was analyzed by the team of researchers in order to map out the Milky Way's shape.

It has been thought to be quite similar in appearance to Andromeda. Recently, however, there have been some indications that it may be a barred spiral instead.

There are at least 50 billion galaxies in the universe. Until quite recently, astronomers placed that figure at only 10 billion. However, thanks to the excellent vision of the Hubble Space Telescope, galactic count estimates were revised substantially in 1996.

Map of our Milky Way galaxy, a spiral galaxy with a short bar at the center.

These extraordinary results were obtained by researchers from the Space Telescope Science Institute in Baltimore, using the Hubble's wide-field camera. By magnifying a tiny sliver of the sky in the vicinity of the Big Dipper, they saw thousands of galaxies where none had been seen before. Statistically, this is an indication that the universe is far more populated than once thought.

The galaxies in space are not distributed uniformly. Rather, they tend to

Quasars

One might think that galaxies, with their billions of stars, would be the brightest, most energetic formations in the universe. Not so. Deep in space there are fonts of energy that—though relatively compact—are as powerful as hundreds of galaxies. These concentrated light sources have been known to radiate energy in the form of radio waves and are known as quasars: short for quasistellar radio sources. (This name is somewhat misleading, however, because many quasars do not emit radio signals.)

Quasars were discovered in 1963 by the Dutch astronomer Maarten Schmidt. Schmidt, working at Mount Wilson Observatory, was observing an especially bright, highly focused radio source called 3C 273. Originally this object was thought to be a star within the Milky Way. Schmidt proved that it must lie far outside the galaxy, and estimated its distance to be 2 billion light-years away. Having proven that it is so distant, he then estimated its absolute brightness to be that of hundreds of millions of stars. Soon thereafter hundreds of other quasars were found.

No one knows with certainty the origins of these powerful beacons. The most prominent theory maintains that they are the bright compact cores of young galaxies in the process of formation. Their intense blasts of power would be produced, in this model, by the

be found in bunches. Along with the Milky Way, for instance, are a number of galaxies, of various shapes and sizes, that are loosely bound together by gravity. These include Andromeda, the Magellanic Clouds, the Sagittarius dwarf, and several dozen other galaxies that are organized in what is called a *galactic cluster.* As these clustered galaxies journey through space, they tend to travel in unison, never moving very far apart from one another.

There are numerous clusters in space, encompassing the bulk of galaxies. Ours is called the *Local Group.* Others include the Virgo Cluster (estimated to be some 50 million light-years away), containing over a

A quasar.

absorption of matter into a supermassive black hole, located in the core's center. As gases fell into the black hole, excess gravitational energy would be radiated away. This would explain how such small sources could give off so much light.

thousand members, and the Coma Cluster (estimated to lie between 300 and 450 million light-years away).

What are the origins of galaxies and clusters? Have they always existed in their present form, or were they fashioned from more primitive entities? To answer these questions, we turn to an examination of the conditions during the early cosmos.

Cosmologists believe that the universe was once much smaller and hotter than it is today. And it was in this compact cauldron that the details of the present-day cosmos were so artfully forged.

CHAPTER SIX

Time's Trigger

After Einstein proposed his theory of general relativity, masterfully describing how the presence of matter relates to the pliability of space, he enthusiastically sought ways of testing his model and then applying it. Without applications, he felt, his theory would be merely an exercise in mathematics, rather than a true representation of physical reality. Specifically, he hoped that his model would describe the behavior of the universe as a whole. With that aim, he set out in 1917 to construct a general relativistic blueprint of the cosmos—a way of mathematically characterizing how the universe appears over time.

His first attempt to fashion a workable cosmology ended in what he saw as failure. Applying his equations of general relativity to the entirety of space, he was dismayed to see that his solution wasn't stable. Unexpectedly, in his model, spatial distances, instead of staying constant, tended to get either bigger or smaller with time, depending on circumstance.

Einstein thought that he made a grave error. Why should the distance between points in the universe change? Space shouldn't just grow or shrink by itself, as if it were a wet wool blanket. There seemed to be no physical reason for this to happen.

To correct his "mistake," he added an extra term to his equations. This addition, which he called the *cosmological constant* term, served to stabilize his equations and guarantee that distances in the universe did not change over time. Adding the cosmological constant seemed to him somewhat makeshift. Nevertheless he could think of no better way to preserve what he saw as the natural stillness of space.

Several years after Einstein advanced his modified model, which came to be known as the Einstein universe, he was surprised to learn about evidence that the cosmos is indeed expanding. Observational data gathered in the 1920s indicated that the universe isn't remaining con-

Artwork titled "Bubble Universe," illustrating the foam- or spongelike structure of the universe.

stant at all, but, rather, is literally flying apart. Presented with this new evidence, Einstein strongly regretted adding the cosmological constant term to his model, calling it the greatest blunder of his life.

These indications that the universe is expanding came about through detailed surveys of galactic distances and speeds, carried out by astronomers Edwin Hubble and Vesto Melvin Slipher. In 1924, Hubble used the Cepheid variable method to determine how far away a number of other galaxies are from the Milky Way. Recall that this technique involves choosing a Cepheid star in a particular galaxy, measuring the intervals between the star's light bursts, and then using this information to determine the star's absolute brightness. From its absolute and apparent brightness readings, the star's distance—and the distance of the star's host galaxy—can then be calculated.

Around the same time that Hubble was preparing his survey of galactic distances, Slipher, working at Lowell Observatory in Arizona, made a remarkable discovery while analyzing galactic light spectra. Slipher was examining light produced by a number of distant galaxies, inspecting their wavelength (color) patterns to try to determine what elements are present. As distinct as human fingerprints, each of the chemical elements—hydrogen, helium, lithium, etc.—produces a characteristic light spectrum of predictable wavelengths. A typical spectral design presents itself as a rainbow of distinct colors. Curiously, Slipher found that the light patterns of the galaxies that he observed were shifted markedly to the low wavelength (red) end of the spectrum. In other words, where he expected orange light, he found red, and where he expected yellow light, he found orange.

Slipher immediately realized that he was witnessing an example of the *Doppler effect*. This effect, discovered in 1842 by Viennese scientist Christian Doppler, involves the shifting in wavelength and frequency of light from a moving source. As Doppler noted, the light from an object moving away from an observer tends to shift toward the red end of the spectrum; the light from an object coming closer shifts toward the blue. Moreover, the faster an object recedes, the redder it looks, and the faster it approaches, the bluer it appears. This is similar to the familiar auditory phenomenon that the sound of a police car's siren grows higher in pitch as the car approaches and lower as it drives away. Because the spectra of distant galaxies are shifted toward the red, Slipher concluded that these galaxies are moving away from us.

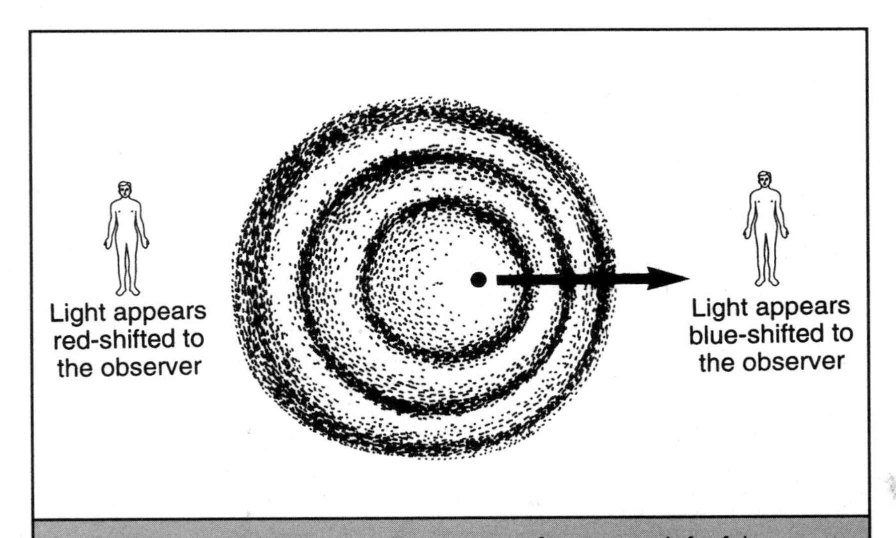

The Doppler effect (center) is the apparent frequency shift of the waves (light or sound) given off by a moving object dot. Objects moving away appear redshifted, and those coming closer, blueshifted. The farther a galaxy is from the Milky Way (and its Local Group), the greater its light is shifted toward the red end of the spectrum.

In 1929, Hubble combined his galactic distance data with the light spectra information gathered by Slipher and noticed a peculiar effect. He discovered that the more distant from us a galaxy is, the greater its radiation is Doppler shifted toward the red end of the spectrum. Thus, the farther out in the universe we look, the more rapidly galaxies seem to be fleeing from us. This implies that galactic recessional (away from us) velocities are proportional to galactic distances, an effect that has come to be known as *Hubble's law.* The ratio between recessional speed and distance has come to be called the *Hubble constant.* The Hubble constant indicates how fast galaxies are receding as a function of distance.

Hubble assumed that the Milky Way occupies no special place in the cosmos. Therefore, because all distant galaxies seem to be receding from the Milky Way, he surmised that they must be moving away from each other as well. He thus concluded that on a large scale every galaxy in the universe is moving away from every other galaxy. (Galaxies bound together in clusters and larger groupings, however, tend to remain close together.)

Astronomers, presented with this strong evidence that the galaxies are speeding away from each other, reached the logical conclusion that the universe is expanding. Space is stretching out like an inflated rubber balloon. Furthermore, assuming this expansion is not a recent phenomenon—and there are many reasons to believe it has taken place for quite some time—space was once much more compact than it is now.

Naturally, there are alternative explanations. None, though, has borne the weight of evidence. The "tired light hypothesis," advanced in 1929 by Fritz Zwicky, states that light waves age as they move through space, and slow down in their rate of oscillation. This reduction in frequency is observed as a redshift. Because, however, there is absolutely no physical reason for radiation to age, this hypothesis has generally been discredited. Another alternative, the steady-state theory of the uni-

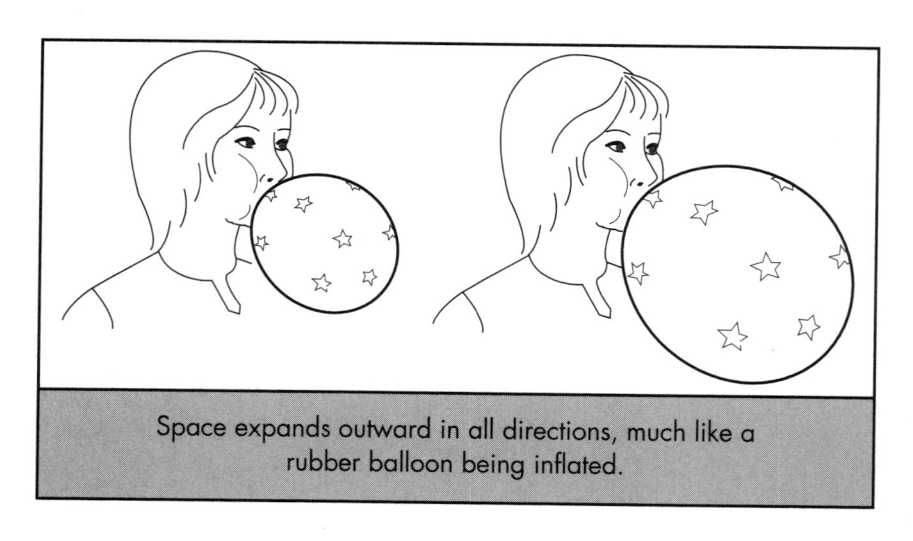

Space expands outward in all directions, much like a rubber balloon being inflated.

The Steady-State Model of the Universe

In 1948, British astronomers Fred Hoyle, Thomas Gold, and Hermann Bondi proposed the steady-state cosmological model as an alternative to theories of expansion from a point. To them, the notion of a Big Bang sometime in the past was distasteful because it meant that all of the matter and energy in the universe was instantaneously created from absolutely nothing.

The alternative they suggested is a universe that is in steady state; that is, it looks basically the same for all times. As galaxies recede, producing observable Doppler red shifts, new matter in minute, undetectable quantities is created to fill in the voids left behind. This raw material, in turn, provides the seeds for new galaxies. Therefore the distribution of galaxies in the universe remains essentially constant.

In the decades since the steady-state model was proposed, evidence has been heaped upon evidence that the universe was once a highly dense fireball. For this reason, the British cosmologists' scheme has few adherents today (though the authors have modified it time and time again in attempts to get it to work).

verse, has similarly been dismissed by most astronomers for lack of solid proof.

As the bulk of scientists became convinced that the universe was once very small, and that it subsequently expanded, they turned to cosmological models that support this view. One such set of cosmologies was developed in 1922 by the Russian theorist Alexander Friedmann.

Friedmann derived his models from Einstein's equations of general relativity, without the cosmological constant term. Because of the exclusion of this stabilizing term, Friedmann's solutions are dynamic rather than static. This flexibility is important for describing a universe in continuous motion.

There are three different kinds of Friedmann cosmologies, known as the open, closed, and flat models. These can be distinguished by their long-term behavior, as indicated by how large they grow (or how small they shrink) over time. Open models start off as a point; the size of the universe in the beginning is zero. As an open cosmos develops, it begins to grow. And once it starts expanding, it continues to do so forever. Like a perpetual adolescent with unrelenting pituitary hormones, nothing can stop its endless growth spurt.

Closed models, in contrast, have a limit to their growth. They begin much the same way as open universes, bursting outward from a speck and expanding in all directions. However, at some point in their histories they slow down in expansion enough that all growth comes to a halt. Ultimately, the same forces that slow the universe's growth cause it to reverse course and shrink back down to a point. This scenario is often called the Big Crunch.

Finally, flat cosmologies fall in between these two categories. They start out much like the other two models. Then, although they always continue to expand, they teeter forever on the brink of collapsing.

To determine which of these models represents our own universe, theorists utilize a physical variable called the *omega parameter.* Omega is a quantity that emerges in Friedmann's solution of Einstein's equations. It is a factor that represents how much mass the universe has—including visible as well as dark matter—relative to the critical amount needed for collapse. The value of omega decides whether the cosmology in question is open, closed, or flat. If omega is less than one, the universe is open and will expand forever. If it is greater than one, then we live in a closed cosmos, which will someday reverse its course and contract to a point. And if omega is precisely equal to one, then space is flat.

Regardless of the fate of the universe, as determined by the omega parameter, its origins would be the same. Astronomers believe that all of the material present in the cosmos today—the stars, planets, interstellar gases, etc.—were once condensed in a "ball" of infinitesimal dimensions and infinite density. Then, during what is called the Big Bang, this ball burst outward from nothingness.

For a long time, the events that took place when the cosmos was

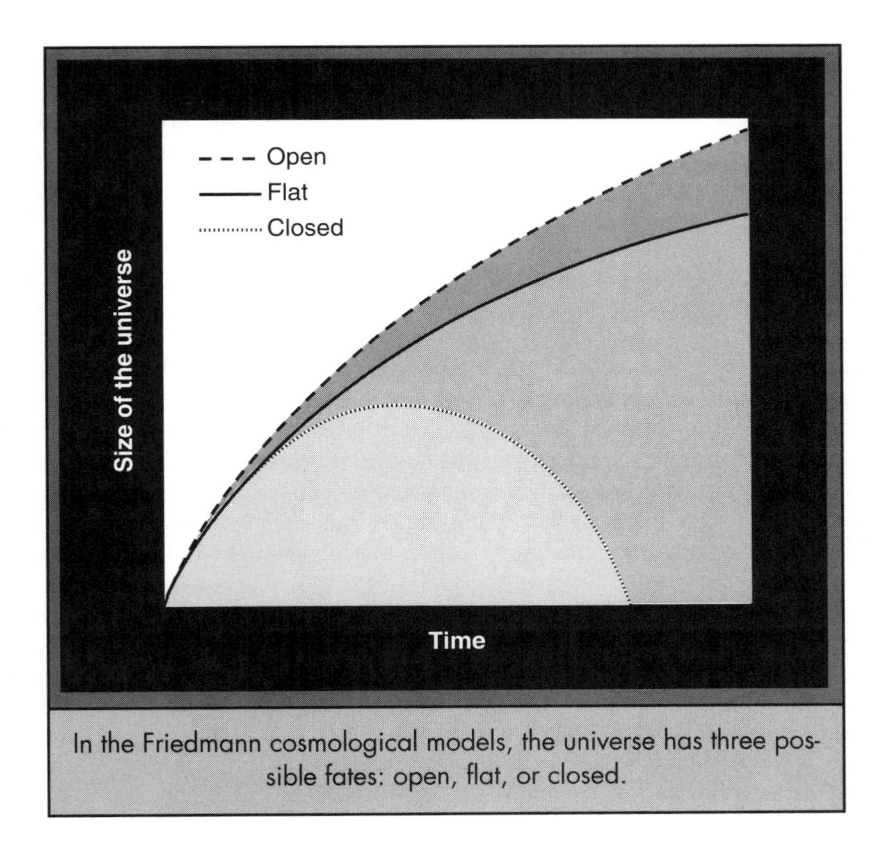

In the Friedmann cosmological models, the universe has three possible fates: open, flat, or closed.

young were shrouded in mystery. Now, thanks to modern particle physics, scientists have a reasonably good picture of what happened during the first minutes of creation. Let's take a look at what has been revealed to have taken place during the early stages of the universe.

We begin at the era of cosmic history a hundredth of a second after the Big Bang. At that time, the universe was incredibly hot; its temperature was over a hundred billion degrees. Because of this enormous temperature, no ordinary matter was present. Atoms and molecules were blasted apart by the heat before they could even be formed. Filling all of space instead was a rich elementary particle "soup," containing, in equal quantities, electrons, neutrinos (particles produced when neutrons decay into protons and electrons), positrons (the positively charged, antimatter counterparts of electrons), antineutrinos (the antimatter counterparts of neutrinos), and photons. More massive particles present in smaller quantities included protons and neutrons, as well as any of the exotic particles that now constitute dark matter.

It is difficult to comprehend how compact the universe was back then. Imagine all of physical reality compressed into a region billions of times smaller than its present extent. The minute dimensions of space didn't last that way for long. In short order, the scale of the cosmos increased rapidly. Within the first few seconds after our original "snapshot," the universe became almost a hundred times bigger.

As the universe grew, the material within it began to cool off. That is because of the physical principle that closed systems undergoing expansion tend to decrease in temperature. This rapid cooling caused several important changes. First, many of the particles present, such as electrons and neutrinos, found it advantageous to unite with their antimatter counterparts. The benefit of combining was that they gained energy in the process. When matter and antimatter unite, they obliterate each other and generate radiation in the form of photons. For this reason, the number of photons increased significantly during this era. Simultaneously, most of the neutrons in the universe converted into protons, electrons, and neutrinos. Therefore, what was left at the end of this era was mainly a sea of photons, speckled with various amounts of protons, electrons, neutrinos, and neutrons, plus rarer particles in smaller quantities.

Our next look at the evolution of the primordial cosmos examines the situation three minutes after the Big Bang. The universe has become significantly cooler than in our last "snapshot." Because its temperature has decreased, particle speeds have slowed down considerably, enabling them to merge to form stable atomic nuclei.

The first nuclei created (aside from hydrogen nuclei, which are simple solitary protons) were those of deuterium, also known as heavy hydrogen. A deuterium nucleus, called a deuteron, consists of a single proton combined with a single neutron. After a time, most of the free neutrons in the universe became locked up into deuterons.

Other simple elements were constructed in this manner from pro-

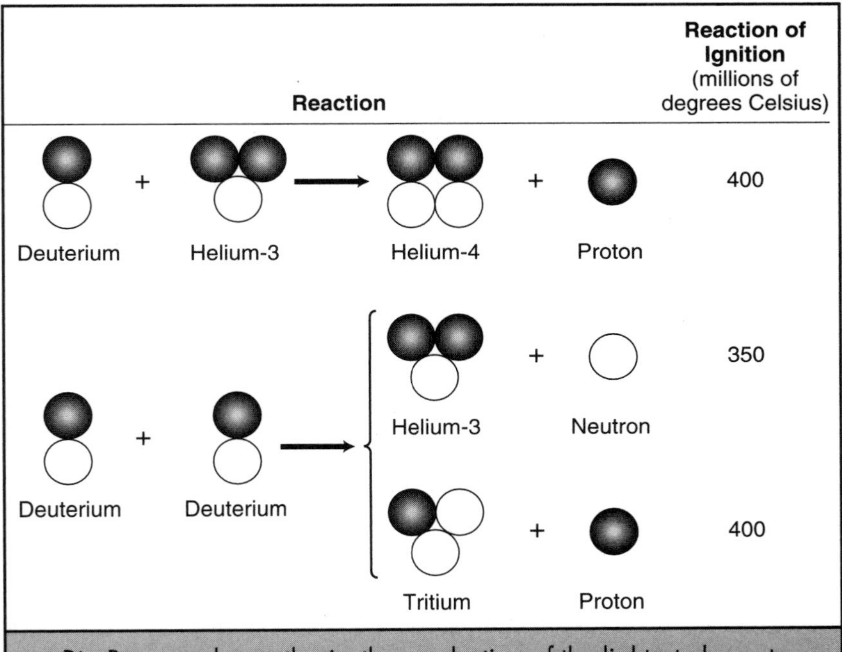

Big Bang nucleosynthesis, the production of the lightest elements through fusion, proceeded from hydrogen to helium to lithium. Then the cosmic temperature dropped and it was no longer viable.

tons, neutrons, and deuterons. Helium-3, a rare form of helium, was fashioned next, as deuterons fused together with protons. Then, as neutrons collided with helium-3, ordinary helium emerged. Step by step, the known assortment of light atomic nuclei—from hydrogen through lithium—were built up from elementary components.

The current abundance of each of these substances provides strong proof of the Big Bang model of the universe. Scientists can estimate how much hydrogen there is in space and compare this figure to the amount of helium. They can then see how well the result measures up to the theoretical prediction of twelve hydrogen atoms for every helium atom. So far, the Big Bang scenario has held up extremely well when put to this test.

Cosmic Inflation

The inflationary universe scenario was developed in the 1980s by theorists Alan Guth of the Massachusetts Institute of Technology (MIT) and Andrei Linde of Moscow University, as well as Paul Steinhardt and Andreas Albrecht of the University of Pennsylvania (all working separately except for the latter two) as a way of addressing several perceived difficulties with the standard Big Bang model. One of these dilemmas, known as the horizon problem, deals with the uniformity of space on the largest scale. Why, this question asks, is the distribution of matter and energy in the cosmos fairly uniform in all directions? What served to smooth out the universe in such a grand manner? A second issue, called the flatness problem, concerns the fact that the cosmological parameter "omega" is so close to one, when in theory it could be any value at all.

The basic idea behind inflation is that the cosmos went through a period of extremely rapid expansion during the very early universe—some 10^{-35} seconds after the Big Bang. Then, somehow, this inflationary period ended, and the slower expansion of the universe that we observe today began.

Inflation solves the horizon problem because it stretches out irregularities. Its phase of rapid expansion resolves the flatness dilemma as well because it forces the universe to become flatter, and hence have a value of omega close to one.

One of the key predictions of inflationary cosmology is that the cosmic background radiation is "scale invariant," meaning that it appears approximately the same no matter on what level it is observed. Evidence from the COBE (Cosmic Background Explorer) satellite has shown this to be the case, lending a boost to a popular theory's prospects.

In 1995, the primordial helium from the Big Bang was directly detected for the first time. Astrophysicists Arthur Davidsen, Gerard Kriss, and Wei Zhang of Johns Hopkins University employed an ultraviolet telescope on board the space shuttle Endeavour to make detailed surveys of the light from quasars. They examined this radiation to look for evidence of absorption of the signal by intergalactic helium. Sure enough, they found characteristic absorption spectral lines (wavelength patterns representing the capture of radiation by helium) that indicated great quantities of this element throughout the universe. The amount of helium found in the region of space that they surveyed corresponded well to the 12:1 hydrogen-to-helium ratio predicted by the standard cosmological model.

Atomic nuclei heavier than lithium's nucleus could not be created in the Big Bang. That is because, by the time lithium was formed, the universe had cooled down so much that the fusion of more massive elements was impossible. All of the heavier elements were forged instead much later in the fiery furnaces of stellar cores.

The next important stage in the evolution of the cosmos was the *era of recombination*. During this period most of the positively charged ions (atomic nuclei) present in the universe gathered up enough negatively charged electrons to form neutral atoms. In the process, a great deal of radiation was released. This release occurred because photons tend to stick closely to charged ions and free electrons, bouncing around between them. Once the ions became neutral atoms, and the electrons were locked into tight orbits around them, the photons became free to move about through space.

From that point on, the cosmos was bathed in a sea of background radiation. At first, this radiation was hot, but as the cosmos expanded, its temperature dropped considerably. Today this primordial energy, cooled down to a frosty 2.735 degrees above absolute zero, continues to permeate the universe as one of the last remaining relics of the Big Bang era.

Scientists are reasonably confident that most of these described events happened. What they don't know yet is *how long ago* these primitive occurrences took place. The question of the age of the universe is one of the most controversial issues in modern cosmology.

CHAPTER SEVEN

The Age Question

Since Hubble discovered the recession of galaxies, astronomers have been trying to measure how old the universe is. Over the years, numerous teams have developed schemes for estimating cosmic age. Their results have clashed explicitly, yielding results ranging from 8 billion years to 20 billion years. This wide spectrum of values has provoked often contentious debates among researchers about astronomical methods.

These astronomers agree, however, that to estimate the age of the cosmos one first needs to obtain the current value of the Hubble constant. Recall that this quantity indicates how fast galaxies are receding with distance. Then, depending on the cosmological model under consideration (open, closed, or flat; with or without cosmological constant), one can determine how old the universe must be to be expanding at its present rate.

The simplest relationship between the Hubble constant and the age of the universe involves the situation in which space is flat—the favored model for inflationary universe theorists. In that case, the Hubble constant is inversely proportional to cosmic age. Accordingly, for flat cosmologies, computing the age once the Hubble constant is known is relatively straightforward. One simply needs to take the mathematical reciprocal.

For a long time the most respected estimate of cosmic age has been that arrived at decades ago by esteemed astronomer Allan Sandage of the Carnegie Observatories in Pasadena, California. Sandage, one of Hubble's students, has been observing supernovas in other galaxies for years, using them as distance gauges.

There are a number of reasons why Sandage finds supernovas to be excellent "standard candles." First of all, supernova blasts are so powerful they can often be seen in distant galaxies. And although for any given galaxy such explosions occur rarely, there are so many galaxies in space

Artist's rendition of a star exploding as a supernova.

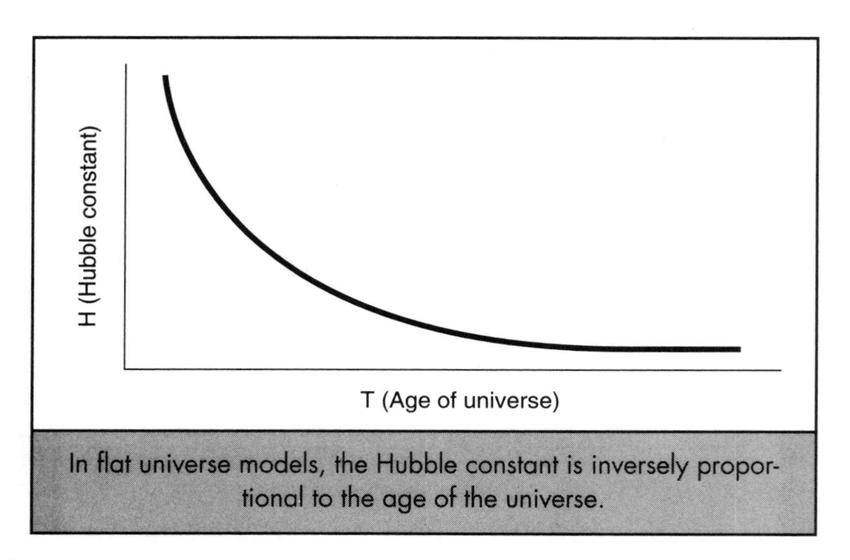

In flat universe models, the Hubble constant is inversely proportional to the age of the universe.

that a new supernova appears somewhere in the sky at least once a week. Finally, certain supernovas, called Type Ia, share approximately the same absolute brightness. Therefore, supernovas of this category have predictable light output, no matter how far away they are. Type Ia supernovas are generally found in elliptical galaxies, as well as in older spiral galaxies.

Sandage's supernova technique is fairly straightforward. By comparing the theoretical value to the measured amount of a supernova's light output, he calculates how far away the supernova is. Naturally, this distance is the same as that of the galaxy that contains it. From numerous galactic distance and velocity readings, Sandage has determined the Hubble constant to be about 50 kilometers per second per megaparsec (1 megaparsec is 3.26 million light-years), and the universe to be between 15 and 20 billion years old.

Over the years since Sandage first made this claim, astronomers have been very satisfied with it. It is large enough to accommodate all the events thought to have taken place in cosmic history. It is much greater, for instance, than the age of the Milky Way—estimated to be between 9 and 12 billion years old.

Recently, though, Sandage's figure has been called into question by a young scientist who works just down the hall from him. Wendy Freedman, along with a 14-member team of astronomers, has developed a new method of estimating the Hubble constant. Her Hubble constant value is much higher than Sandage's—resulting in a much lower estimate of cosmic age.

Freedman's technique—which involves spotting Cepheids in a distant galaxy called M100—depends heavily on the keen vision of the Hubble Space Telescope. Before the Hubble was launched, astronomers freely used the Cepheid variable method as a way of measuring distances to nearby galaxies such as Andromeda. However, they recognized that the limitations of ground-based telescopes made it impossible to record Cepheids much farther out. For this reason, brighter objects, such as supernovas, were seen as more attractive standard candles. Still, researchers hoped to extend the Cepheid technique with more precise instrumentation. They saw the launching of the Hubble Space Telescope as an excellent opportunity to accomplish this goal. Naturally, then, the Hubble was specifically designed to help astronomers hunt for Cepheids in distant galaxies.

Allan Sandage of the Carnegie Observatories in Pasadena, California.

In 1994, Freedman's team aimed the Hubble at M100 and observed more than 40,000 stars for several months. From the data gathered, they pinpointed 20 stars as Cepheids. Once these Cepheids were found, their periods and absolute brightness values were recorded. This information was then used to estimate the galaxy's distance to be 56 million light-years, give or take 6 million.

Astronomers believe M100 to be situated among a group of spirals in the Virgo Cluster of galaxies. Virgo's recessional velocity has been known for years; now, thanks to Freedman and her collaborators, its distance is known as well. One might think that these values could be used directly to find the Hubble constant. However, the Virgo cluster is so close to our own Local Group that there is significant gravitational attraction between the two sets of galaxies. Therefore, Hubble's law—

that galactic recession is proportional to distance—does not fully apply to Virgo. And the value of Hubble's constant obtained by dividing Virgo's velocity by its distance would not be accurate.

To find Hubble's constant, Freedman's team needed to apply a more sophisticated approach—using their M100 results to obtain the distance to the remote Coma cluster. Coma is far enough away from Earth that its motion closely follows Hubble's law. Freedman and her co-workers felt that information about Coma would be ideal for pinning down an accurate value of Hubble's constant.

In their method, they first supposed that the distance found to M100 was the same as that of the average distance to nearby spiral galaxies in Virgo. Next, they looked at a similar set of spirals in the Coma cluster. Assuming that these two sets of spirals have the same intrinsic brightness, they then compared how much dimmer the Coma spirals appeared than the Virgo spirals. From this comparison, they determined Coma to be 5.5 times farther away than Virgo, implying that Coma is slightly over 300 light-years from Earth. Finally, they divided Coma's known recessional speed by its distance and came up with a Hubble constant value of 80 kilometers per second per megaparsec. They realized that they could be as much as 20 percent off, due to uncertainties in their estimate of M100's location in Virgo.

Freedman's Hubble constant estimate is much higher than Sandage's. Consequently, it leads to a much lower figure for the age of the universe. If Freedman is correct, then the cosmos is only 8 to 12 billion years old. The fact that there is a large range of values stems from uncertainties in Freedman's calculations, as well from lack of knowledge about whether the universe is open, flat, or closed.

For most scientists, this age estimate seems absurd. Some of the oldest stars in the universe are thought to be at least 14 billion years old. Surely, the stars in the cosmos cannot be older than the space that contains them. After all, someone cannot be older than his own mother.

Today, one of the most pressing issues in cosmology is the resolution of the age question. To account for the discrepancy between the estimated ages of the universe and its components, a number of theorists are hard at work trying to revise the standard cosmological model. Some are suggesting a revival of the cosmological constant term; a few are even scrapping the Big Bang model (or general relativity) altogether.

The distance to the M100 galaxy in the Virgo cluster was measured using the Hubble Telescope.

Others believe that the age estimates rendered by Freedman and her supporters are inaccurately low and should be dismissed. Truly a sense of urgency is in the air.

Resolving the age dilemma ultimately requires a detailed understanding of the large-scale composition of space. To that end, astronomers are busily mapping out portions of the cosmos in an attempt to fathom its organization and history. Just as our ancestors recorded on parchment the intricate topography of Earth, modern-day "cartographers" are using astronomical instruments to develop a portrait of a universe rich in structure and diversity.

CHAPTER EIGHT

The Transgalactic Bubble Bath

During the age of exploration of the sixteenth to eighteenth century, thousands of vessels sailed up and down the world's rivers, straits, and coastlines. One of the primary missions of explorers on board these ships, aside from the quest for raw materials, was to map out the features of the Earth. The monarchs of Europe required the best maps possible in order to strengthen their territorial claims and to gain the upper hand in battle. Therefore, they funded and supported lengthy exploratory voyages to little-known regions. It took time to complete this map making, and many errors had to be corrected along the way. Even as late as the turn of the nineteenth century, Australia was thought to be a chain of islands rather than a continent.

Over the years, through improved cartography, a more sophisticated understanding of our world emerged. We slowly learned more about the relative sizes and positions of the oceans and continents and how they meshed together throughout the globe. This detailed knowledge led to important insights.

As an example of how maps have inspired advances, consider the case of the German geologist Alfred Wegener. In 1912, Wegener pointed out that the outlines of the continents seem to fit together so snugly that they must at one time have been connected. For example, South America and Africa seem to fit together like interlocking pieces of a jigsaw puzzle. Therefore, Wegener suggested that the continents once belonged to a single mass, called Pangaea, and that since they have been drifting apart for millennia. Wegener's insight—based on his reading of well-constructed maps—triggered the modern science of plate tectonics (the study of continental drifting).

Today, human frontiers extend much farther than the reach of the ocean waves. Like our ancestors, we must once again map out great areas of unexplored territory—in this case, the cosmos itself. Scientists hope that a complete depiction of the visible universe will help them to understand its dynamics, in the way that knowledge of the world map inspired Wegener's theory of continental drifting.

Mapping the cosmos has been one of the greatest challenges in modern astronomy. There are a number of reasons why this task has proved demanding. First, a two-dimensional atlas is insufficient for scientific purposes. To fathom the complex interplay between the various large structures of the universe, astronomers need to know more than just positions of bodies in the sky. They require, in addition, information about how far away these bodies are.

Unfortunately, it is difficult to determine the distances to objects beyond a certain range. We have discussed several different ways of finding out how far away celestial bodies are. For nearby stars, the method of parallax is sufficient. For distant stars in our own galaxy, though, the technique of comparing apparent brightness to absolute brightness must be employed.

To measure the distances to neighboring galaxies and clusters, scientists must use more sophisticated means, such as the Cepheid variable method. Before the launching of the Hubble Space Telescope, Cepheids were used as yardsticks almost exclusively for galaxies within the Local Group. The Hubble has made it possible to extend this approach to nearby clusters. We have seen how Wendy Freedman used this technique to measure the distance to Virgo.

Still, there are regions in which Cepheids are too faint to observe. In these nether provinces, science is forced to engage in a bit of guesswork. The *Tully-Fisher relation,* an observational principle relating the absolute brightness of a galaxy to the width of a particular line in its light spectrum (the red wavelength line, for example) is sometimes used as an alternative. More commonly, astronomers measuring the large-scale proportions of the universe turn to Hubble's law of proportionality between galactic velocities and distances. By measuring how far a galaxy's (or cluster's) spectral lines are shifted toward the red, observers can estimate how far away the galaxy is. Until Hubble's constant is better known, however, this law can provide only relative distances.

Hubble's law is a simple proportionality to only a billion or so light-years. When astronomers try to reach out even farther with their measuring rods, they encounter the problem of time delay. Light from bodies

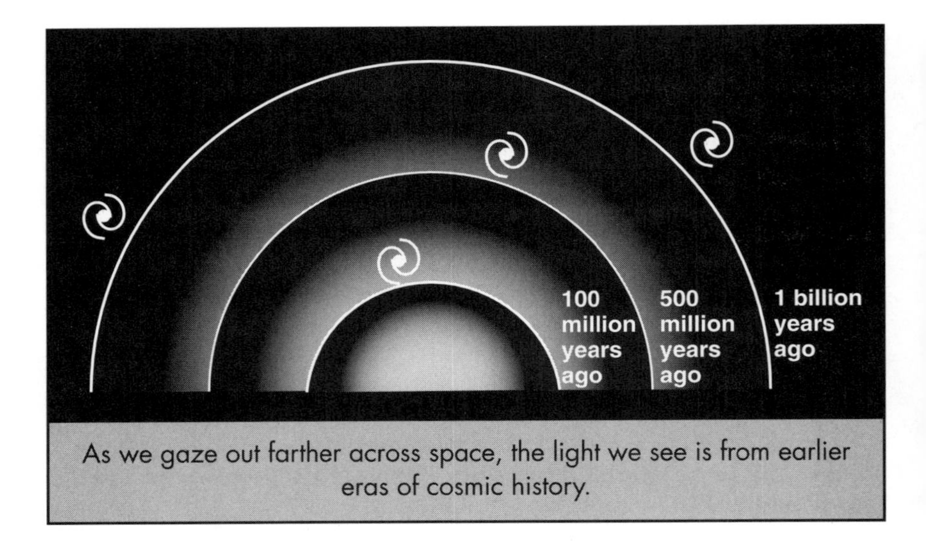

As we gaze out farther across space, the light we see is from earlier eras of cosmic history.

billions of light-years away takes billions of years to reach us. Therefore, it provides us with a snapshot of the way the cosmos looked billions of years ago—not the way it looks at present. Theorists believe that eons ago the Hubble constant had a different value. Thus, in any assessment of the distances of objects believed to be billions of light-years away, researchers must estimate what they think the Hubble constant was then, not what it is now.

All together, the hodgepodge of yardsticks used for large-scale distance measurements, from parallax to Cepheids to spectral methods, is known as the *cosmological distance ladder.* Rung by rung, scientists have used this stepladder to climb from the familiar domain of nearby stars to the distant regions of galactic clusters and quasars. As new measuring rods have become available, this ladder has been strengthened and extended, becoming an increasingly formidable connection to the cosmos.

In addition to the distance measurement issue, astronomers face another difficulty when attempting to map the visible universe: the territory to cover is incredibly vast. The volume of space that can potentially be inspected with a telescope is well over ten quadrillion quadrillion light-years and is full of tens of billions of galaxies (most of them found by the Hubble Space Telescope only recently). It will take centuries to catalogue these objects.

Meanwhile, one of the most important ongoing projects of astronomers such as Margaret Geller and John Huchra of the Harvard–Smithsonian Center for Astrophysics is to obtain representative cross sections of the visible universe. Ideally, these observed portions of space

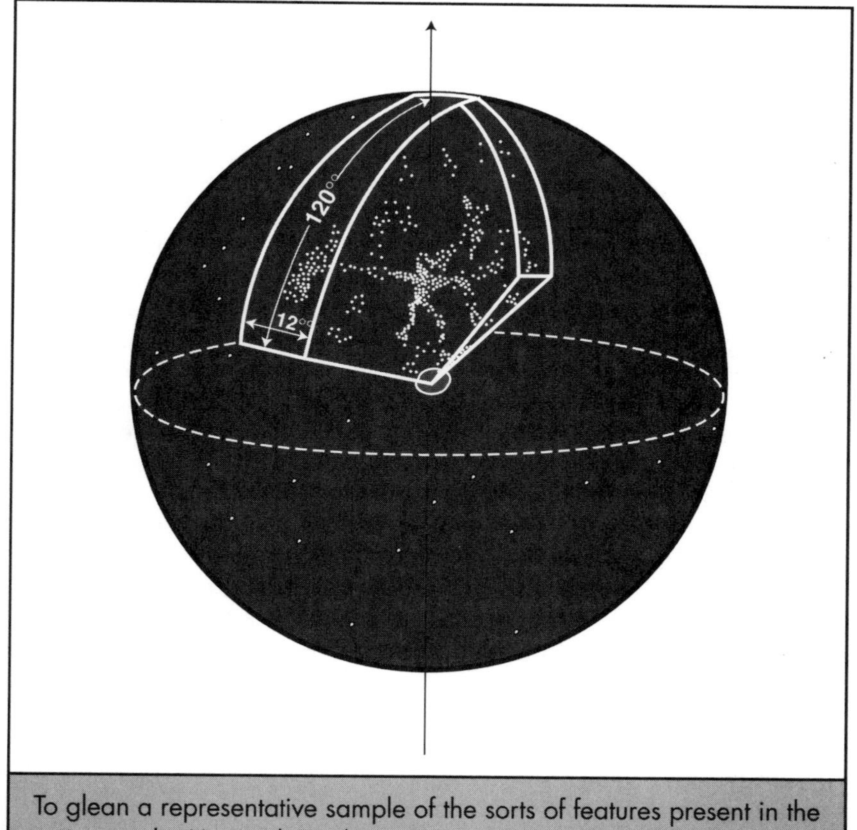

To glean a representative sample of the sorts of features present in the universe, the Harvard–Smithsonian team divided space into wedges.

serve to provide us with a rough idea of how the galaxies in the universe are distributed. From this picture we may better understand the origins and nature of order in the cosmos.

The sample sets that the Harvard–Smithsonian team have chosen consist of three-dimensional slices of space. They chose the form of a wedge in order to obtain pictures of the universe that have the widest diversity.

The first representative region in the project was mapped out by Geller, Huchra, and Valerie de Lapparent during the spring of 1985. They determined the spatial positions of approximately 1,100 galaxies, located on a 6-degree-wide strip. They chose this size in order to be able to finish their survey in a short period of time. The results they obtained were intriguing.

Going into the survey, Geller and her colleagues didn't expect to see evidence of large-scale order in the universe. In fact, they thought that their sky scan would reveal an evenly textured cosmos. They believed that they would see galaxies and clusters scattered uniformly throughout, much like the sprinkling of raisins throughout raisin bread. Instead, they found striking proof of curious galactic patterns. Galaxies and clusters, rather than presenting themselves randomly, appeared to be organized into long, spindly strings and broad, extensive sheets, as well as into mammoth bubbles of matter. The interiors of these bubbles looked strangely empty, as if all of the galaxies within were siphoned out with a straw.

The Harvard–Smithsonian group were most surprised by the sheer contrasts that they saw. Next to thickly populated regions of space, teeming with millions of galaxies, were domains—voids they called them—containing practically nothing. Somehow, at some period in the history of the cosmos, large-scale order had emerged out of chaos. And the team couldn't explain why or how this happened; they simply observed it to be the case.

In 1989, Geller and Huchra extended their survey to include several thousand galaxies. This time, they observed an additional feature: a "wall" of galaxies that stretched out more than a half a billion light-years through space. This barrier, called the *Great Wall,* is the largest single structural feature known to exist in the cosmos.

Geller and her co-workers were far from the first to notice large-scale patterns in the universe. In the 1950s, French astronomer Gérard de

Vaucouleurs generated a flood of controversy with his suggestion that galaxies and clusters belong to greater objects called "supergalaxies" (now called *superclusters*).

At the time, most astronomers believed that clusters were the largest groupings possible in space. They felt that gravitational theory, as expressed by Einstein's general relativity, would not favor larger units to form. More extensive structures, it was thought, would be bound together so weakly by gravity that the expansion of the universe would pull them apart. Therefore, they would last only briefly, and would not exist today.

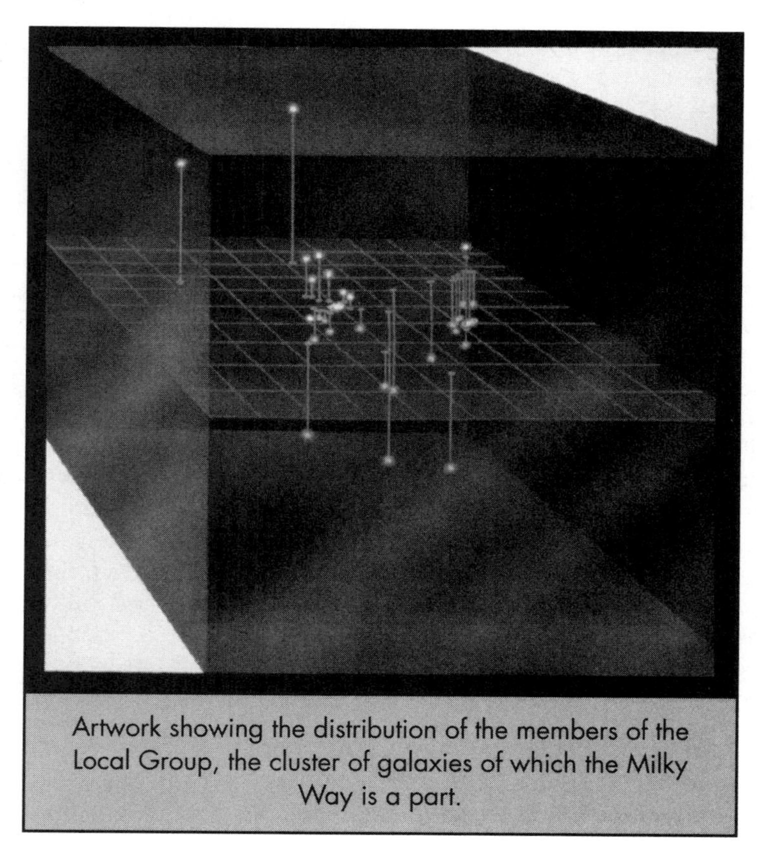

Artwork showing the distribution of the members of the Local Group, the cluster of galaxies of which the Milky Way is a part.

Over the years, however, the astronomical community has grown to accept the existence of "clusters of clusters." Our Local Group of galaxies has been shown to belong to a chain called the *Local Supercluster,* centering on the Virgo cluster, and stretching out a hundred million light-years through space. Other superclusters have been found as well, criss-crossing the universe with their beaded strands.

De Vaucouleurs, an impatient firebrand in his youth, now feels a sense of vindication. The world has finally caught up with him. He realizes now that it takes time for changes in perspective to sink in. As he has remarked, "Just as a growing child progressively becomes aware of larger units of human organization—family, neighborhood, city, etc.—astronomers have come in the past 400 years to recognize the hierarchical arrangement of the heavens. This astronomical growing-up is still in progress."

Today, based on overwhelming observational evidence, such as that supplied by Geller, Huchra, and de Lapparent, most astronomers accept the fact that the cosmos possesses a complex structural hierarchy. Descriptive terms such as "filament," "bubble," "sheet," and "void" have become integral parts of their vocabulary. Rather than arguing whether or not the universe has large-scale structure, they agree that it does, and they seek to understand the source and nature of this organization.

Essentially, there are three models of structure formation in the universe. They differ in their answer to the question, Which came first, galaxies or larger structures? One approach, nicknamed the "pancake model," was proposed in the early 1970s by Soviet scientist Yaakov Zel'dovich. The pancake model is a top-down theory, meaning that it supports the view that large structures, such as sheets and bubbles, were created first, and then that these broke up into superclusters, clusters, and, finally, galaxies. Specifically, in Zel'dovich's approach, the early universe was full of large, flattened lumps of matter, "pancakes," that eventually fragmented into smaller pieces. Finally, these pieces evolved into galaxies. Zel'dovich's model explains very well why galaxies are arranged in long strands and thin sheets; these structures are the remains of the original "pancakes."

A second approach, called hierarchical clustering, has, among its advocates, Princeton astrophysicist Jim Peebles. In this bottom-up model, galaxies, shaped out of gas clouds, were created first in the prim-

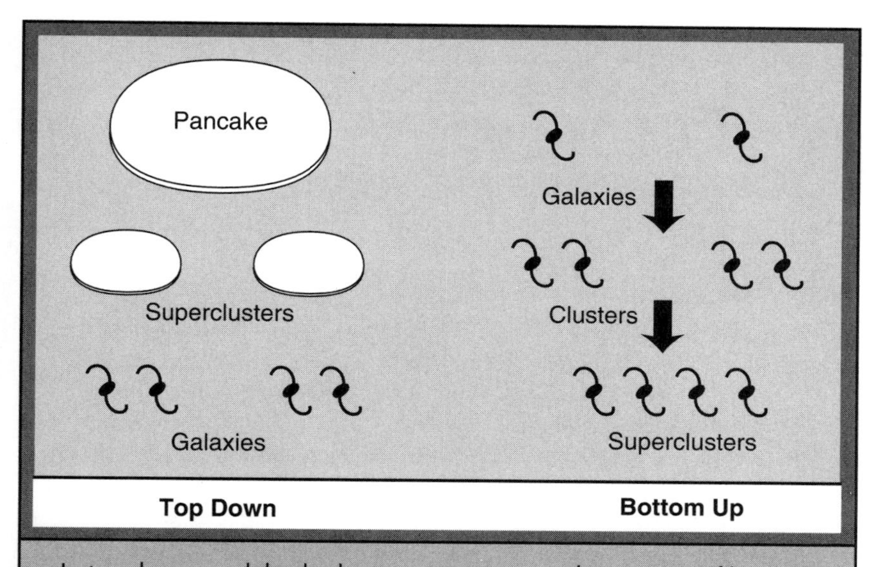

In top-down models, the largest structures, such as cosmic filaments and sheets, are formed first. These structures fragment into individual galaxies. Bottom-down models, in contrast, describe the possibility that galaxies are created first. These coalesce into more complex formations, such as clusters.

itive cosmos. As the universe developed, many of these galaxies came close enough together to exert gravitational pulls on each other. Pretty soon groups of galaxies came together, forming clusters, and then superclusters. And, in a manner analogous to winter winds piling up snow in snowdrifts and leaving other areas snow-free, voids were formed in the spaces in which all matter was drawn away by gravity.

Finally, a third model of structure formation is called the fractal approach. Fractals are objects that are self-similar; that is, they look basically the same on all scales of observation. They are similar in this way to the Russian painted dolls that are embedded one within another. According to the fractal approach, many levels of structure, from galaxies to clusters to superclusters, were created at the same time. Superclus-

The Great Attractor

Every profession exploring the frontiers of knowledge has its mythic figures. In contemporary cosmology, the Seven Samurai, an international group of dedicated galaxy watchers, certainly form the stuff of legend. In 1987 this multifaceted research team, consisting of David Burstein of Arizona State University, Roger Davies of the National Optical Astronomy Observatories, Alan Dressler of the Carnegie Institute, Sandra Faber of the University of California at Santa Cruz, Donald Lynden-Bell of Cambridge University, Robert J. Terlevich of the Royal Greenwich Observatory, and Gary Wegner of Dartmouth College, convened for the purpose of looking for general patterns in the velocities of galaxies.

Their results were extraordinary. They found strong evidence that a large group of galaxies, 200 million light-years away from Earth, are being deflected in the direction of a point in space where nothing seems to lie. This point, dubbed the *Great Attractor,* appears to act as an enormous invisible mass, exerting a strong gravitational pull on a huge region of space.

Over the past decade, scientists have tried to develop a satisfactory explanation for the Seven Samurai's findings. Some researchers have surmised that the *Great Attractor* is the expression of a new form of matter that is impossible to see. Others favor an answer that is far more mundane (and that seems to be supported by recent Hubble Telescope findings): the *Great Attractor* represents the collective force of many dim galaxies in that region.

ter formation, then, was a manifestation of the same process that shaped galaxies—only on a greater scale.

Recently, theorists, such as James Gelb and Edmund Bertschinger of MIT, have been using the method of computer simulation to test models of galaxy formation. In their models, they seed a "toy" cosmos with randomly distributed chunks of matter and observe the effects of gravity and other forces on these seeds. They have been able to simulate fairly well the creation of galaxies and other structures as long as they include in their studies the presence of a material called *dark matter* (to be discussed in Chapter Nine).

Dark matter is any substance that possesses mass without giving off noticeable radiation. Many scientists estimate that over 90 percent of the universe is composed of invisible material of unknown composition. Only by taking the interaction of dark matter with ordinary matter into account can the process of structure formation be fully understood. Accordingly, to resolve the issue of how the cosmos has been shaped, the mystery of its "missing mass" must first be unraveled.

CHAPTER NINE

Ghosts in the Void

In the classic novella *The Invisible Man,* by H. G. Wells, a man discovers a potion that renders himself transparent to light. When he drinks this concoction, his body fades out of view, and only his clothes can be seen. If, at the time of taking an afternoon stroll, he is wearing only his hat, his gloves, tennis shoes, and a pair of glasses, that's all the rest of the world would see walking down the street. People might well conclude, while observing this spectacle, that an invisible man is connected to all these things, making them move.

Yet several years ago there was a fad item—called "invisible dogs"—made for people who couldn't afford (or didn't want) real pets, but still enjoyed the thrill of walking them. There were specially made leashes designed to bob up and down as their human "owner" took the dog for a walk.

Suppose a reasonable adult saw one of these "invisible dogs" coming down the street; might they think something exists there that doesn't meet the eye? Of course not. Someone seeing such an "animal" might wink and pretend to pet it, but wouldn't conclude that it really exists.

The way that stars move in galaxies, and that galaxies move in clusters, seems to indicate that far more is out there than meets the eye. But what is it that is tugging on these celestial bodies? Is it something real, like the Invisible Man's body in the Wells story? Or is it an illusion, like the form of the faddish "invisible dog"? Almost certainly it is the former. Mountains of evidence have piled up in recent years that dark matter exists in abundance through the cosmos.

Scientists have suspected for decades that the nature of stellar and galactic motions cannot be entirely explained by the action of the gravitational force generated by its visible matter. In the early 1930s, Dutch astronomer Jan Oort studied the behavior of stars in the outer reaches of the Milky Way with the aim of understanding their dynamics better. In particular, he measured the stars' distances above and below the galactic disk, and calculated how much mass the Milky Way would have to contain to hold onto the stars at these heights and depths. Like weights attached to springs, stars in the galaxy tend to bob up and down; the amount of their motion is dependent on their gravitational attraction to the rest of the Milky Way. Curiously, Ort found that the amount of mass in the Milky Way needed to produce these effects is at least three times that of the sum total of its visible material.

Around the same time as Oort's star studies, work by Swiss-Ameri-

Fritz Zwicky, Swiss-American astronomer who postulated that most of the mass in the Coma Cluster is invisible.

Vera Rubin of the Carnegie Institution of Washington plotted galactic rotation curves and found evidence of dark matter.

can astronomer Fritz Zwicky provided even stronger evidence that there is more to the universe than can be seen. Zwicky analyzed the behavior of galaxies in the Coma Cluster to find out how much mass was needed to provide the gravitational force to bind it together. To his surprise, he calculated the mass required to be *three hundred times* what is observed. He surmised by this that most of the matter in the Coma Cluster is dark.

Perhaps the most convincing early proof of the existence of dark matter was provided in the 1970s by Vera Rubin and her colleagues at the Carnegie Institution of Washington. They examined what is called *galactic rotation curves:* the orbital speeds of stars and gases in a galaxy plotted against their distances from the center.

In our own Solar System, planetary rotation curves, the plotted speeds of planets versus how far away they are from the Sun, are well described by Kepler's laws. Because most of the matter in the Solar System is concentrated in its center—namely, the Sun—planetary velocities show a sharp decrease with increasing distance. Thus, Pluto orbits the Sun far more slowly than Mercury does.

If the mass of a spiral galaxy, such as the Milky Way, were distributed according the visible arrangement of galactic material, then a similar drop-off would be seen. Because most of the mass would be in the central bulge, gravity would be weaker in the halo. Consequently, away from the center, stellar velocities would decrease with distance—resulting in a galactic rotation curve that dips sharply.

However, this has not turned out to be the case for the Milky Way, Andromeda, and other spirals. Instead of decreasing with distance, the galactic rotation curves for these galaxies tend to plateau. In other words, stellar velocities remain constant throughout the halo. This indicates that the mass of each of these galaxies, rather than being concen-

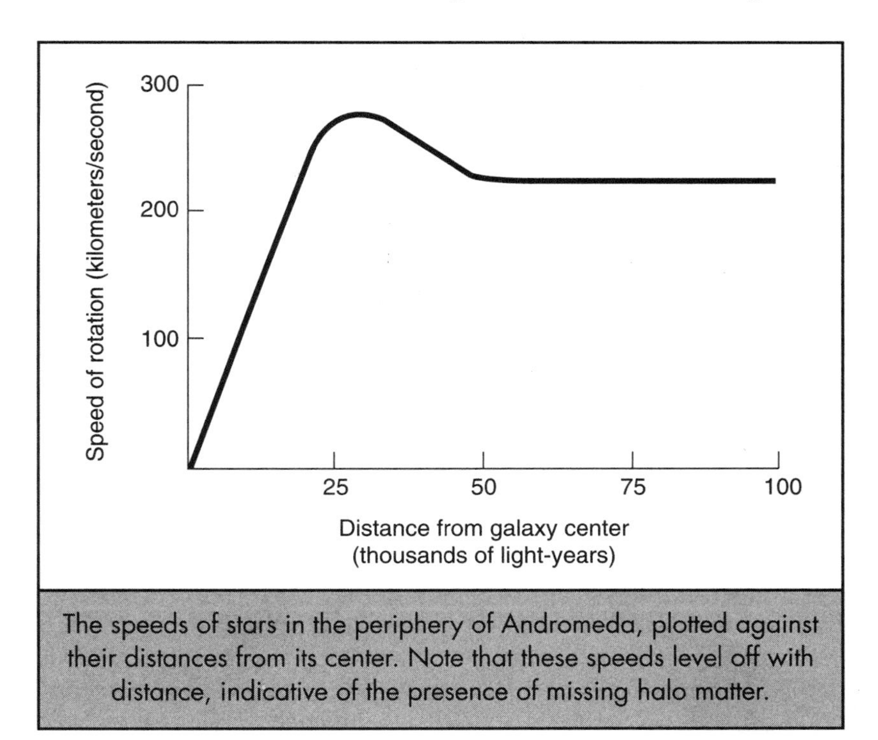

The speeds of stars in the periphery of Andromeda, plotted against their distances from its center. Note that these speeds level off with distance, indicative of the presence of missing halo matter.

trated in the galactic bulge, is spread fairly evenly throughout. For this to be the case a considerable amount of dark matter must be present in galactic halos.

Other studies, too numerous to mention, have provided further proof that over 90 percent—and perhaps as much as 99 percent—of the cosmos is composed of material that cannot be directly observed by telescope. Dark matter appears to abound within the domains of galaxies. Experiments have also shown it to be present in the spaces between galaxies. It even seems to exist within galaxy-free parts of space, such as the interiors of voids. Voids may not really be voids after all.

It is sobering to think that after centuries of telescopic observation, only a fraction of the matter present in the universe has been mapped. Astronomers have seen only the tip of the iceberg. Here, this cliché is apt—like icebergs, it seems to be the case that most of the universe is perpetually hidden from view, and only a meager 10 percent or so lies "above the surface."

What is this mysterious substance that dominates the cosmos? Various theories have been proposed in recent years about its nature. The favorite candidates can be divided into three major categories: massive compact halo objects (MACHOs), weakly interacting massive particles (WIMPs), and massive neutrinos. In spite of their connotations, the first two terms do not refer to the manliness of the material in question, but rather to where it can be found.

MACHOs are dense bodies present in the peripheral regions of galaxies. These objects give off no discernable radiation and make their presence known only through their gravitational interactions with other entities. The first known examples of these dark bodies were discovered in 1993 by three teams of astronomers: a French group called EROS, a Poland-based group called OGLE, and an American-Australian collaboration called the MACHO project. The third group, the largest, was headed by Charles Alcock of Lawrence Livermore National Laboratory, along with David Bennett of Lawrence Livermore and Kim Griest of the University of California at San Diego. Their search used the 5-foot-diameter telescope at the Mount Stromlo Observatory near Canberra, Australia.

Each group found distinct examples of gravitational lensing by MACHOs of distant stars in the Large Magellanic Cloud. Gravitational lensing is a general relativistic effect in which material situated between

Earth and a distant object affects the appearance of the object. Recall that according to general relativity, heavy matter can bend light, and even focus it like a lens. In this case a MACHO temporarily stood between the Earth and a red giant from the Large Magellanic Cloud, concentrating, for a time, light picked up on Earth from the star. This amplified signal was recorded and analyzed by the astronomers, who used the data to determine the mass and extent of the MACHO. The presence of MACHOs in the Milky Way was indicated by the temporary brightening and diminution of the light from these stars. In the case of the U.S.–Australia team, a red giant was observed to increase its apparent radiation yield for a period of 33 days before settling down to its previous level of light output. After other possible reasons for this behavior were ruled out, the event was determined to be a signal of the gravitational lensing of an invisible but massive object.

At a January 1996 meeting of the American Astronomical Society, the American–Australian collaboration reported strong evidence that much of the Milky Way's halo is composed of MACHOs. This proof came in the form of the discovery of seven new massive halo objects. Once again, the researchers used gravitational lensing of the Large Magellanic Cloud to ascertain the properties of these elusive bodies.

The size and mass of each of these MACHOs range from one-tenth the mass of the Sun to the mass of the Sun. Because of their smallness and dimness, it is probable that most of them are white dwarfs. They likely originated as main-sequence halo stars, similar to the Sun, that subsequently used up most of their nuclear fuel. They remain as stars that shine so weakly that they can barely be detected.

There is also a chance that some of the MACHOs are red dwarf and/or brown dwarf stars. Red dwarf stars are exceedingly cool and emit little radiation. Therefore, they are very difficult to detect directly. Brown dwarfs produce even less light. They represent stars that lack the critical mass for fusion to begin; hence, they do not burn. Other possible MACHO candidates that have been proposed by theorists include Jupiter-sized planets, neutron stars, and black holes. It is likely that MACHOs comprise a mixture of some, or all, of these bodies—with the vast majority being white dwarfs.

Scientists now believe that MACHOs account for roughly half of all galactic dark matter—perhaps even more. Unfortunately, that still leaves a significant portion of the invisible material in galaxies left to explain, not to mention substantial quantities of dark matter in the rest of the cosmos. Therefore, researchers have suggested that the remaining dark matter in the galaxy is composed of WIMPs.

WIMPs comprise a broad category of hypothesized objects that share the feature that they rarely interact with ordinary matter. These include axions (massive particles that have been proposed in theories of the early universe), supersymmetric particles (see the box opposite) and other exotic types of subatomic particles.

How might WIMPs be detected? Some scientists are trying to locate them with gargantuan atom smashers, colliding conventional particles at ultrahigh speeds in the hope of finding unusual byproducts.

Daniel Snowden-Ifft, Eric Freeman, and Buford Price of the University of California at Berkeley believe they have found a better way. They are examining a small sample of mica that is half a billion years old for signs of the impact of WIMPs. Subtle chemical transformations within the rock would provide telltale evidence of scarring from past WIMP collisions.

According to particle theory, if a WIMP were to impact on a piece of rock, it would have some chance—albeit a small one—of displacing one of the rock's atomic nuclei. The displacement of this nucleus would likely, in turn, cause electrons from other atoms to be knocked out of place. Gradually, over time, a trail of altered atoms would form through the rock. These are the chemical changes that the Berkeley researchers hope to detect.

So far the team has tested only a small portion of the rock—about 8 percent of a 1-square-millimeter sample—and WIMP tracks have not yet been observed. To improve their chances, they are now looking at a larger sample, hoping to find proof that these elusive particles exist.

Recently, a dark matter suspect that was almost dismissed—the neutrino—has become a contender once more. In the 1970s, the ordinary neutrino, produced during nuclear decay, topped everyone's list of candidates for the missing substance in the cosmos. At that time, though the neutrino was thought to have zero or near-zero mass, its exact value was unknown. Theorists calculated, however, that if the neutrino were to have even the slightest mass, the dark matter problem would be solved. That is because there are myriad neutrinos in the cosmos, and, if each

Supersymmetry

Supersymmetric particles, the hypothetical by-products of a particle physics model known as supersymmetry theory, have often been suggested as dark matter candidates. Supersymmetry theory attempts to unite the two major categories of particles in the universe: fermions and bosons.

Briefly, fermions provide the building blocks of matter. Protons, neutrons, and electrons, the constituents of atoms, are all fermions. Bosons, on the other hand, supply the glue that sticks fermions together, as well as the explosive force that pushes them apart. Photons, carriers of the electromagnetic force, and gravitons, conveyers of gravity, are examples of bosons.

According to models of supersymmetry, each fermion has a bosonic companion, and vice versa. For example, the bosonic equivalents of electrons are called selectrons. The fermionic "soul mates" of the proton and graviton are referred to, respectively, as protino and gravitino.

So far there is no empirical evidence that these companion particles exist. However, many theorists find supersymmetry to be an elegant way of bridging the divide between the two major classes of subatomic bodies. They are hoping that these new particles—photinos and the like—will turn up shortly in the data from the highest energy accelerators. If so, then the dark matter mystery may indeed have a speedy resolution.

had a mass, the total would be enormous. Sadly, experiment after experiment (aside from a little-believed Russian result in 1980) seemed to indicate that the neutrino was massless. The neutrino could no longer be considered a viable contender.

In 1994, the near-beaten candidate made a brilliant comeback. Los Alamos physicists, led by Hywel White, used a tank full of mineral oil and a series of 1,220 phototubes (light detectors) to measure the masses

The enormous neutrino detector at the Brookhaven National Laboratory, Long Island, New York.

of decaying neutrinos. These neutrinos were caught in the act of transforming into other particles, a process known as oscillation. As they decayed they gave off light in distributions that depended on their masses. This radiation was picked up by the detectors and analyzed by the scientists.

The fact that the neutrinos can metamorphose in such a manner indicates that they are massive objects, like electrons. Massless bodies cannot change form. Massive particles, in contrast, have the possibility of decaying if conditions are right.

The mass range inferred for the neutrino by the Los Alamos team is between 0.5 and 5 electron volts. (One electron volt corresponds to the energy equivalent of about one billionth of the mass of a proton.) There are so many neutrinos in space—billions per cubic foot—that, assuming

Dark Matter: Cold, Hot, or Mixed?

Astrophysicists are engaged in a lively debate about the temperature of the dark matter in the cosmos. The reason this is such a hot issue (excuse the pun) is that models of structure formation in the universe require, as a given, an estimate of the average speed of its material content. Average speed and temperature are directly related; hot materials consist of more rapidly moving particles, on average, than cold substances. Hence, hot dark matter fragments would travel faster, and create larger, more spread-out structures, than would bits of cold dark matter.

For a long time, models of the universe, including cold dark matter (WIMPs, for example), were popular structure formation scenarios. Computer simulations were run with these models, which well reproduced the creation of galaxies. The main problem with this approach was that it failed to simulate the proper large-scale distributions of galaxies.

Hot dark matter scenarios (including, for instance, the presence of massive neutrinos) were found, on the other hand, to predict faithfully the common large-scale forms in the universe: superclusters, bubbles, walls, and voids. Unfortunately, though, they failed to model the production of galaxy-sized objects.

Currently, most scientists favor an eclectic approach, involving a mixture of cold and hot dark matter. Not only do mixed models better reproduce what is known about the universe's structure, they also correspond well to contemporary ideas about its particle content. MIT astrophysicist Edmund Bertschinger has found that a combination of 80 percent cold dark matter and 20 percent hot dark matter, such as neutrinos, has worked very effectively in computer simulations of galaxy formation.

they do have mass, their total mass could possibly outweigh all of the known galaxies put together.

Most scientists are now convinced that dark matter is far from being a single substance. In the past few years strong experimental evidence has emerged for the existence of MACHOs. There have been some indications, as well, as for the prevalence of massive neutrinos. WIMPs, though not yet detected, seem important ingredients for theoretical models of the evolution of galaxies and other cosmic configurations. Dark matter, then, could mean any or all of these things.

To understand the role that matter and energy played in the formation of structure in the universe, we must examine how these substances were distributed during the early moments of the Big Bang. Fortunately, modern radio astronomy provides us with a window on this era. A remarkably detailed profile of the primordial cosmos can be seen in an analysis of the microwave background radiation that pervades all of space. The discovery of this radiation more than 30 years ago was a fortuitous event indeed—enabling science for the first time to study the intricate structure of the Big Bang.

CHAPTER TEN

Light Show

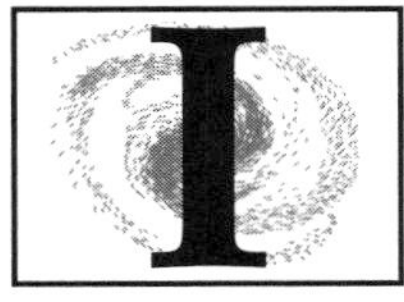

In 1964, two Bell Laboratory researchers, Arno Penzias and Robert Wilson, made an astonishing discovery that proved to be the long-sought confirmation of the Big Bang theory. Their result—the detection of the cosmic background radiation—was even more remarkable for being wholly unexpected.

While using the 20-foot-diameter radio dish at Holmdel, New Jersey, to search for microwaves from the Milky Way, Penzias and Wilson were disturbed by a strange sort of persistent "buzz." The noise wouldn't go away no matter how much they tried to correct it. At first they attributed this "hum" to the presence of pigeons in the base of the receiver. Penzias thought that their excreted "white dielectric material," as he put it, was interfering with the incoming signals. The team cleaned the dish thoroughly, but the static remained. Finally, they were forced to conclude that they were picking up real signals from deep space.

In the late 1940s, physicists George Gamow, Ralph Alpher, and Robert Herman had suggested in a series of articles that the detection of the cosmic background radiation would be important proof of the Big Bang hypothesis. They estimated its present-day temperature to be about 3 K (3 degrees above absolute zero). Robert Dicke performed the same calculation in the 1960s and immediately realized the source of Penzias and Wilson's hum. Apparently, they had discovered the cooled-down radiation from the creation of the universe. Penzias and Wilson were later awarded the Nobel Prize for their achievement.

One notable feature of this radiation—which was reassuring in some ways and disturbing in others—was its extraordinary smoothness. No matter what direction they turned their radio dish, the microwaves detected had the same temperature. This uniformity was confirmed in experiment after experiment during the late 1960s and early 1970s.

In some sense, astronomers were glad that the cosmic background

Arno Penzias and Robert Wilson, joint discoverers of the cosmic microwave background radiation.

radiation was evenly distributed in temperature throughout the sky. This meant that it is truly a universal effect, rather than a local phenomenon, linked only with individual galaxies or with some particular part of the universe. For this reason, researchers were sure that this energy dates all the way back to the era of recombination of the Big Bang rather than stemming from a more mundane source.

On the other hand, the microwave temperatures were found to be much too uniform for comfort. Theories of structure formation in the universe require minute variations in the radiation background. These tiny fluctuations were not to be seen.

This prediction of cosmic background fluctuations stems from what the majority of scientists believe to be the source of structure in the cosmos. According to most galactic formation models, from the top-down approach of Zel'dovich to the bottom-up scenario of Peebles, the seeds of present-day structure were planted in the early cosmos as density irregularities. In other words, the universe at the time of the era of recombination must have had denser regions, as well as areas that were more sparse. Over time, the thicker zones attracted more and more matter through their stronger gravity, and grew into what we now know as galaxies, clusters, superclusters, sheets, and filaments. Smaller lumps grew into larger lumps, and so on. In contrast, the domains that were

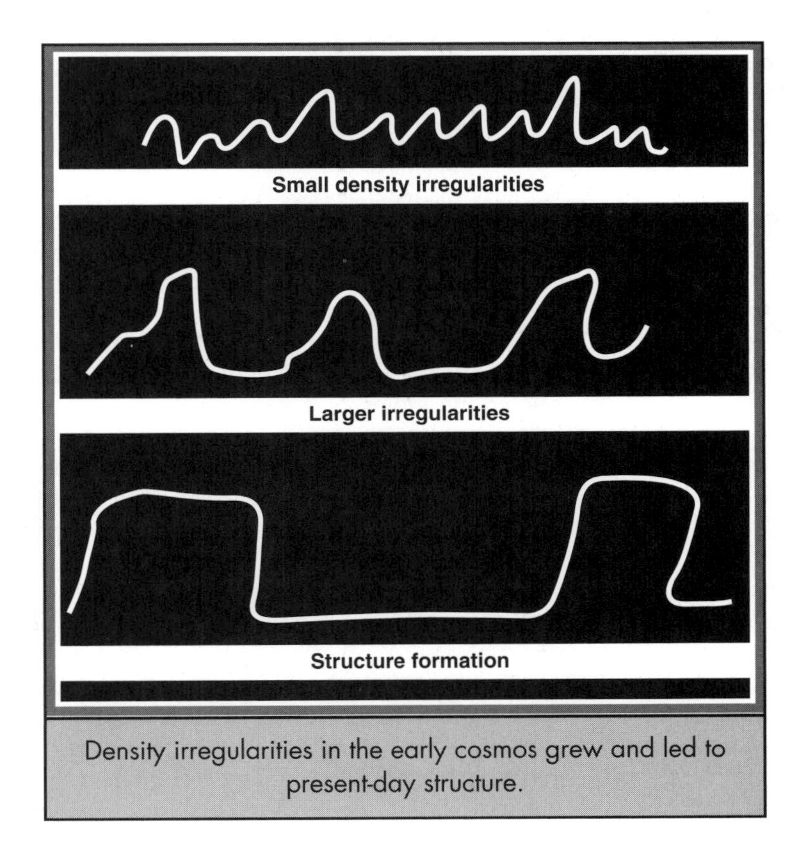

Density irregularities in the early cosmos grew and led to present-day structure.

less dense had less gravitational pull and became what we observe as the spaces between galaxies, such as voids.

Physicists have calculated the size of the irregularities needed during the recombination era in order to have formed structure of the sort we see today. They have estimated that there must have been approximately a tenth of a percent variation in the density of the primordial cosmos. In other words, certain regions must have been a tenth of a percent more concentrated, and others a tenth of a percent more spread out, than the average.

Furthermore, according to astrophysical theory, the temperature variations of the radiation released during the era of recombination are directly related to the density fluctuations of the matter density during that period. For this reason, theory requires temperature "ripples" in the cosmic microwave background, reflecting similar hills and valleys in material distribution.

In 1977, astronomer George Smoot and his team from Lawrence Berkeley Laboratory and the Space Sciences Laboratory of the University of California at Berkeley produced the first evidence of variations in the temperature of the background radiation. These differences, however, were not the long-sought primeval "ripples." Rather, they represented a phenomenon called the "dipole anisotropy."

The dipole anisotropy is a Doppler effect due to the forward movement of the Milky Way through the sea of cosmic microwaves. Like a ship thrusting toward oncoming waves as it voyages across the ocean, our galaxy continually presses through wave fronts in the cosmic microwave background. Due to Doppler shifting, the sky's microwave radiation in the forward and backward directions (relative to the Milky Way) seems altered. It appears slightly hotter ahead of our galaxy and slightly cooler behind it.

These subtle temperature differences were picked up by the Berkeley group's sensitive radiometers (radio wave detectors), placed high up in the atmosphere on board a National Aeronautics and Space Administration (NASA) Ames U-2 jet. For the purpose of maximizing their ability to sense the dipole anisotropy, these detectors were aimed in opposite directions. To everyone's delight, the signals that they recorded corresponded closely to theoretical predictions for the Doppler effect.

Once Smoot found these dipole fluctuations, he began to plan out a

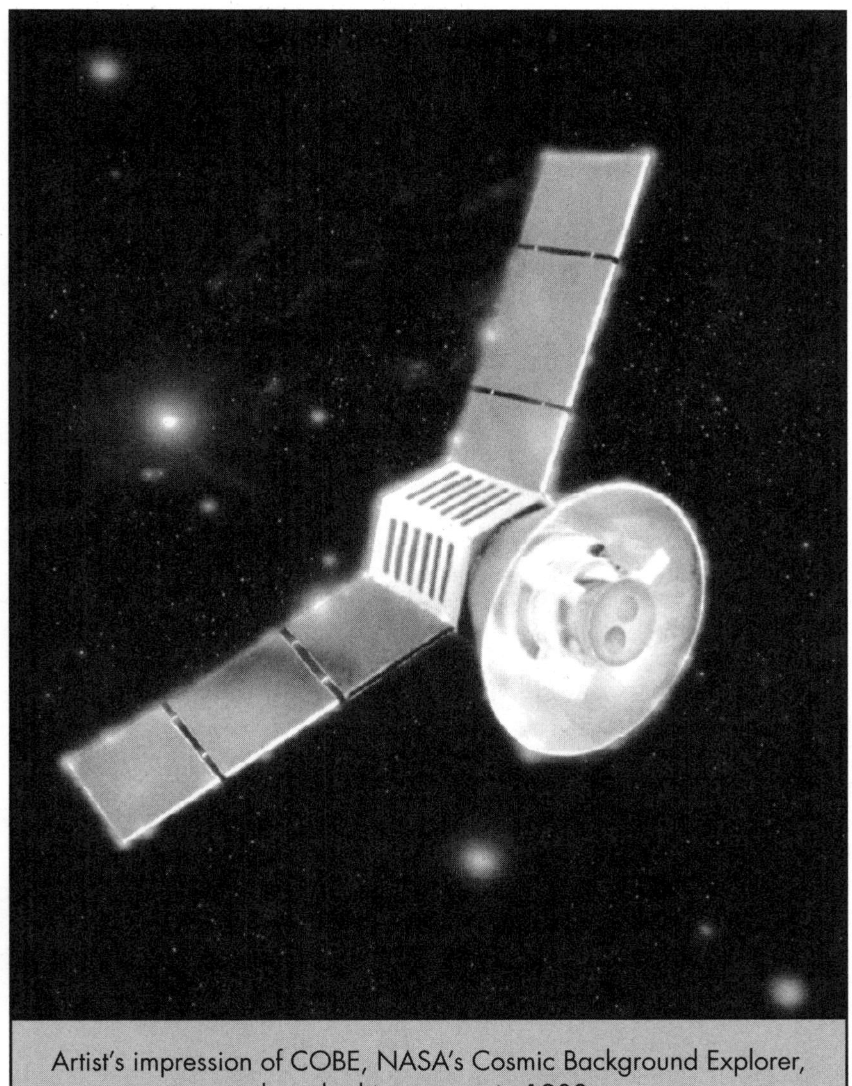

Artist's impression of COBE, NASA's Cosmic Background Explorer, launched into space in 1989.

search for the true relic variations from the early universe. With that aim in mind, he designed a special high-precision detector, called the differential microwave radiometer (DMR). The DMR is unique among such instruments because, instead of recording the temperature of a single point, it uses a pair of antennae to measure the temperature difference between two different regions of the sky. This allows for more precise numerical readings than other radiometers can muster; it can measure temperature differences of one part in a million.

The DMR actually contains three separate radiometers, tuned to three different radio bands. These frequencies were chosen because they represent parts of the spectrum in which the cosmic radiation background greatly dominates all other signals. For example, at these wavelengths, the cosmic background is more than a thousand times stronger than galactic microwave emissions.

Once Smoot finished building the DMR, he prepared it to be launched into space. Because of setbacks in NASA's programs due to the Challenger space shuttle disaster, it took a number of years for him to obtain clearance for his program. Finally, in late 1989, Smoot and his colleagues obtained the go-ahead from NASA to carry out their mission. The DMR was launched in November of that year on board a satellite called the Cosmic Background Explorer (COBE). COBE was placed into orbit high above the distorting effects of Earth's atmosphere, but well below the equally troublesome charged particles in the Earth's radiation belts.

In 1992, Smoot made the long-awaited announcement of the discovery of relics in the cosmic background—hot and cold regions of space over 100 million light-years across. The temperatures in these zones varied about a hundred thousandth of a degree from an average temperature of 2.735 degrees. In other words, these variations amounted to roughly six parts per million.

Astronomers immediately recognized Smoot's results as strong evidence in support of the Big Bang model. The average radiation temperature that he found corresponds precisely (out to six decimal places) to theoretical predictions for the cosmic background norm. Furthermore, the variations that he discovered measure up well to the values theorized by structure formation schemes. Finally, his results provide solid evidence for the abundance of dark matter in the universe. All in all, the

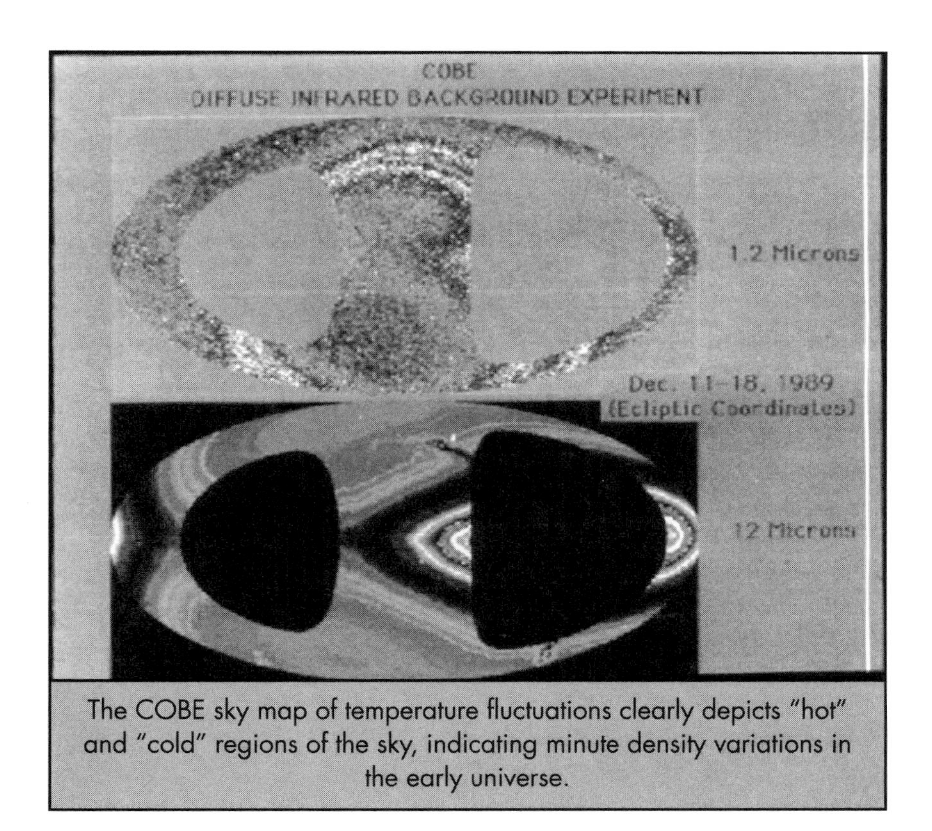

The COBE sky map of temperature fluctuations clearly depicts "hot" and "cold" regions of the sky, indicating minute density variations in the early universe.

findings of Smoot and his colleagues represent one of the great triumphs of late twentieth century cosmology.

Equipped with detailed information about the radiation profile of the early universe, astrophysicists have been busy revising theories of structure formation. While some are trying to develop enhanced models of how galaxies developed from primordial seeds, others are reaching back even further in time and attempting to explain the origins of these lumps themselves. They are pondering how these minuscule irregularities arose in just the right size and number to provide the primitive foundations of cosmic structure.

Currently, there are several leading theories about the source of pri-

Up, Up, and Away

The COBE satellite sky scan has been far from the only successful look at the cosmic microwave background fluctuations. Balloons, though they obviously cannot be hoisted as high as satellites, have nevertheless proven to be popular instrument carriers. The reason is that balloon missions are much cheaper and easier to plan out than satellite expeditions.

In 1989, a balloon-borne instrument searched the skies over New Mexico for 12 hours, taking detailed microwave background temperature readings. A team of scientists from MIT and Princeton University took almost four years to analyze the measurements from this detector, finally presenting their results in February 1993. Much to everyone's relief, their data corresponded closely to the COBE temperature maps.

Other balloon missions have attempted to do COBE one better, by searching for finer structural detail in the microwave background than COBE has revealed. The more delicate measurements may tell us more about the period of the universe called the era of recombination, a time in which cosmic radiation was freed up and structure began to form. Examples of such balloon-based scans include MAX (Millimeter Anisotropy Experiment) and MSAM (Medium-Scale Anisotropy Measurement), each launched in the early 1990s.

mordial density fluctuations. One prominent scheme involves the *inflationary universe* paradigm. According to this scenario, the cosmos went through a period of extremely rapid growth early on in its history. Following this tremendous surge, it then settled down to the much slower pattern of expansion that we see today.

Inflationary cosmology describes a method by which the seeds of galaxies may have been formed. These irregularities arose, according to inflationary schemes, as minuscule *quantum fluctuations,* produced during the genesis of the universe. (Quantum fluctuations are microscopic energy fields that quantum mechanics predicts must spontaneously arise in any tiny space.) Next, these fluctuations were stretched out during the universe's growth spurt, greatly magnifying in size. Eventually, they became large enough to form the seeds of cosmic structure.

An alternative to the inflationary approach is the theory of *textures.* Textures are hypothetical "defects" in the fabric of the universe, believed to have been produced during what is called a phase transition. Phase transitions (sudden changes in form due to temperature variation) abound in nature; liquid water, for instance, becomes solid ice when its temperature is lowered. The universe is thought to have undergone similar changes as it cooled down. As it grew cooler, its energy fields likely became altered. Perhaps, in a manner similar to the way cracks form in ice when it freezes quickly, textures—fissurelike forms—developed among the rapidly changing force fields of the early universe. Then, according to this model, cosmic structure grew up around the textured regions of space.

These are but two of the theories of cosmic structure that have sprung up in recent years. As the profile of the microwave background radiation becomes better known, scientists can better distinguish among these approaches. Because this body of data is growing so rapidly, humankind will likely soon understand the complete process by which structure was created in the universe.

The Fate of the Universe

Starting with the discovery of Penzias and Wilson, the final third of the twentieth century represents banner years in the history of cosmology. We have been able to reach out more remotely in space and to push back farther in time than anyone could have imagined merely decades ago. Truly, we stand on the threshold of a deeper, richer knowledge of the universe than ever before.

There is much we have learned so far in our search for the truth about the far beyond. We know now that the cosmos was once immensely hot and unimaginably small. Furthermore, when it was very young, we surmise that it was uniform—or that somehow any major irregularities were smoothed out during an age of inflationary growth. Yet, in spite of this overall regularity, the cosmos must been speckled with the tiny seeds of the precursors to galaxies.

At some point in the past, simple atoms were formed and cosmic radiation became free to permeate all of space (and to be mapped eventually by Penzias, Wilson, Smoot, and others). In time, the newly created atoms flocked to denser parts of the universe—perhaps to regions full of massive dark matter. Structure was built up as giant clouds of hot material coagulated into galaxies, clusters, and superclusters. At the same time, larger features, such as cosmic bubbles, filaments, and voids, as well as the prominent Great Wall, began to take form. All the while, as the universe continued to expand, these objects grew more and more distant from each other. The background radiation, in turn, became cooler and cooler.

Soon, the galaxies began to produce stars. The first stars—Population II—were formed mainly from hydrogen gas. As they died out, often in fiery explosions, a group of younger stars—Population I—were fashioned from their ashes. Some of the latter types of stars were formed with planetary systems. A fraction of these planetary systems supported the development of intelligent life. And on one of these planets, called Earth, you have just read this chronicle of your world.

Scientists are reasonably confident that most of these described events happened. Based on evidence collected by astronomers and physicists over the past 30 years, especially information regarding the cosmic microwave background, as well data concerning the present-day quantities of known elementary particles, the Big Bang is now understood fairly well.

Yet, as well as astronomers think they comprehend the origins of the universe, they are still highly uncertain about its destiny. Is the cosmos open, closed, or flat? (These are the choices exhibited by the Friedmann models discussed in Chapter Six.) In other words, will it expand indefinitely, expand for a while and then recontract someday, or totter forever on the brink between these two extremes?

If the cosmos were open or flat, its ultimate fate would be one of absolute quiescence. Gradually, as the universe continued to expand, more and more stars would use up their nuclear fuel and turn into white dwarfs, neutron stars, and black holes. The white dwarfs would eventually burn out completely and become the lifeless orbs known as black dwarfs. Finally, with the death of the last shining star and the evaporation of black holes through the Hawking process (see Chapter Four), no usable energy would be left in space. Without the driving force of stellar power or the energy derived from any other fuel source, all physical processes would come to a complete halt. This final state, called *heat death,* would constitute the end of time itself.

If the cosmos were closed, on the other hand, its waning era would be far more dramatic. At some point in the distant future, its Hubble expansion would cease and turn into a universal contraction. All of the galaxies in the sky would reverse course and move toward each other as space collapsed in on itself. Finally, in an event much like a time-reversed Big Bang, the universe would implode into a singularity, a region the size of a mathematical point.

Theorists have shown that these different possibilities are delineated by the parameter omega, which represents how much mass there is in the universe relative to the critical amount needed for cosmic recollapse.

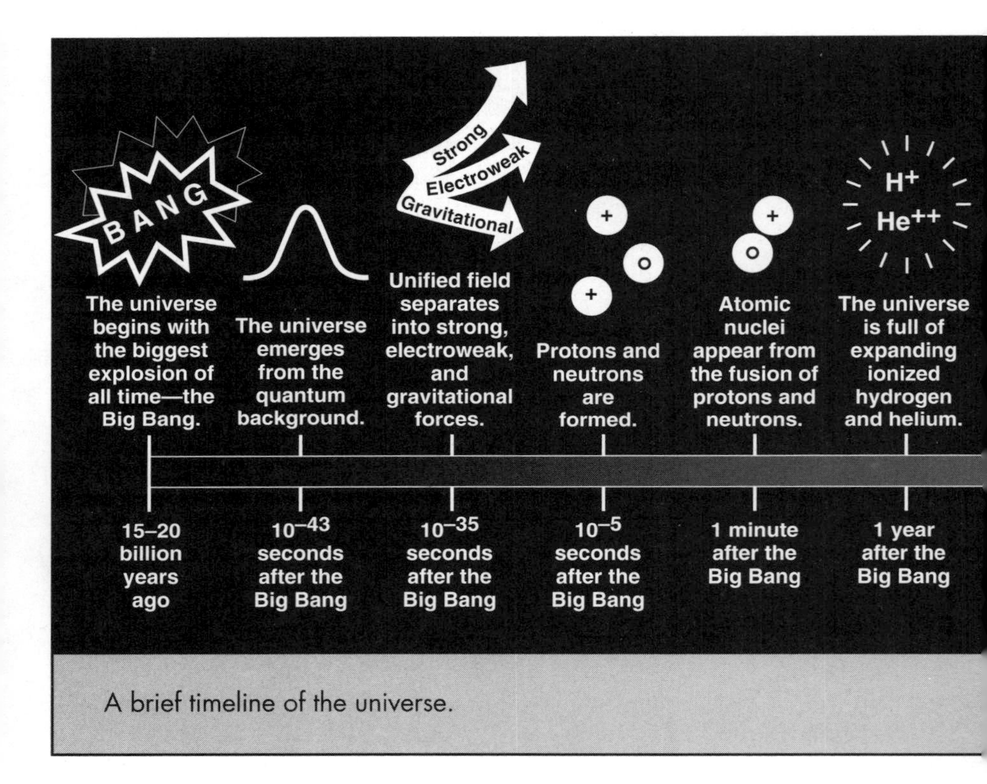

A brief timeline of the universe.

There are several methods by which astronomers are currently attempting to determine omega's value.

One of these ways is to gauge how much luminous and dark matter there is in the universe. Researchers have already established that the luminous matter alone would not be enough to close the universe. Moreover, based upon current findings, they estimate that not enough of the amount of dark matter required for a flat or closed cosmology exists in space. These results suggest that the universe is open.

It is far too soon, though, to draw a conclusion from this about the ultimate fate of the cosmos. First, the study of nonluminous material is

still in its infancy. As we have discussed, astronomers' assessments of the nature and quantity of dark matter have been revised as new data have been collected. With each reassessment, their cosmic mass estimates have been similarly updated.

Moreover, this method of calculating the value of omega depends on an exact determination of the critical mass of the universe. Unfortunately, though, the critical mass parameter is a function of the Hubble constant. Because astronomers have yet to pin down the Hubble constant, they are uncertain about the critical mass as well.

To circumvent these obstacles, a British–American team of scientists, led by Saul Perlmutter, Carl Pennypacker, and Gerson Goldhaber of the University of California at Berkeley, is trying to find omega by an independent approach. They are seeking the value of a related constant, called the *deceleration parameter*, defined as a function of the rate by which the expansion of the universe changes over time. Its value, for a Friedmann cosmology, is precisely one half that of omega. Therefore, deceleration parameters of less than one half, equal to one half, and greater than one half, respectively, represent cosmologies that are open, flat, and closed.

The method of the British–American group involves employing the powerful Isaac Newton telescope in the Canary Islands, off the northwest coast of Africa, to measure the redshifts and distances of faraway supernova explosions. The supernovas they are studying are so remote that their light has taken billions of years to reach us. Therefore, these objects represent an earlier period in the universe's history—one in which presumably the Hubble expansion was different. The British–American group hopes to record this difference, calculate the deceleration parameter, and then use this value to predict the fate of the cosmos.

Contemporary astronomers often find themselves enmeshed in the web of a curious paradox. In accordance with general relativity, they seek the destiny of the universe by analyzing the distribution of its material content. Yet, to understand how this matter is distributed, they often make assumptions about the long-term behavior of the universe—whether it is open, closed, or flat. For example, the inflationary paradigm requires that the universe be flat at present.

To break free of this predicament, researchers are learning to become more open-minded about the shape and structure of the cosmos—to eschew all unnecessary assumptions about the nature of the Big Bang. Many are turning to "designer models" of the universe that incorporate, without contradiction, current assessments of its age, structural hierarchy, and material distribution. These novel theories are specifically tailored to accommodate cosmological data as presently understood. Often these approaches depart from the Friedmann models and harbor unusual features, such as Einstein's abandoned cosmological constant term. Only future experimentation will tell if such radical departures are necessary.

It is surely an exciting time to study the structure of the universe. On the one hand, much has been learned in recent years about stars, galaxies, and other astronomical objects. And it seems as though the Hubble Space Telescope is making new discoveries almost every few weeks. On the other hand, situations like the age question, the dark matter dilemma, the mystery of the Great Attractor, and the issue of the fate of the universe have caused ordinarily confident scientists to scratch their heads in befuddlement. As the cosmos becomes more familiar, it seems increasingly bizarre. It is enough to make you want to grab a telescope, run out into the night air and see for yourself what is going on.

FURTHER READING

Bartusiak, Marcia, *Thursday's Universe* (New York: Times Books, 1986).

Friedman, Herbert, *The Astronomer's Universe: Stars, Galaxies and Cosmos* (New York: Ballantine Books, 1990).

Halpern, Paul, *The Cyclical Serpent: Prospects for an Ever-Repeating Universe* (New York: Plenum Press, 1995).

Harrison, Edward, *Cosmology* (London: Cambridge University Press, 1981).

Lightman, Alan, *Ancient Light: Our Changing View of the Universe* (Cambridge, MA: Harvard University Press, 1991).

Sagan, Carl, *Cosmos* (New York: Ballantine Books, 1980).

Silk, Joseph, *The Big Bang: The Creation and Evolution of the Universe* (San Francisco: W. H. Freeman, 1980).

Smoot, George, and Kay Davidson, *Wrinkles in Time* (New York: William Morrow, 1993).

Weinberg, Steven, *The First Three Minutes: A Modern View of the Origin of the Universe* (New York: Basic Books, 1977).

INDEX

I N D E X

INDEX

Photo Research: *Beth Krumholz, Laurie Platt Winfrey, Carousel Research*

Abbreviations:
NASA = National Aeronautics and Space Administration
PR = Photo Researchers
SPL = Science Photo Library
STSCI = Space Telescope Science Institute

p. 2—courtesy NASA

p. 3—© D. Berry/STSCI

p. 4—detail of p. 18, © Osterreichiriche National Bibliothek, Vienna

INTRODUCTION

p. 12—courtesy Yerkes Observatory, University of Chicago p. 13—© Hank Morgan/Science Source/PR p. 14—courtesy NASA

CHAPTER 1

p. 17—© Culver Pictures, Inc. p. 18—© Osterreichiriche National Bibliothek, Vienna p. 19—© Culver Pictures, Inc. p. 20—above, PR; below, © Culver Pictures, Inc. p. 23—Inquisition scene by Nicolo Barabino, Palazzo Celesia, Genoa; © American Heritage p. 27—© Laurie Platt Winfrey, Inc. p. 29—© NBC Photo

CHAPTER 2

p. 31—© Laurie Platt Winfrey, Inc. p. 33—© Julian Baum/SPL/PR p. 34—© Mehau Kulyk/SPL/PR p. 39—© David A. Hardy/SPL/PR

CHAPTER 3

p. 41—© Royal Observatory, Edinburgh/SPL/PR p. 42—© Hale Observatories/Science Source/PR p. 43—courtesy Naval Research Laboratory/SPL/PR p. 44—© John Foster/Science Source/PR p. 47—© Julian Baum/SPL/PR p. 48—© Jill Fineberg/PR

CHAPTER 4

p. 50—© UPI/BETTMANN p. 51—© STSCI/NASA/Mark Marten p. 52—© Sanford Roth/PR p. 53—below, © Tony Craddock/SPL/PR p. 55—© Joe Sohm/PR p. 56—© UPI/BETTMANN p. 57—below, © Ray Nelson/Phototake NYC

CHAPTER 5

p. 59—© David A. Hardy/SPL/PR p. 60—© Sanford H. Roth/PR p. 61—courtesy Smithsonian Library p. 62—courtesy Smithsonian Library p. 64—top, © California Institute of Technology; middle, courtesy Mt. Wilson and Palomar Observatories; bottom, © D. Berry/STSCI p. 67—© J. Baum & N. Henbest/SPL/PR p. 69—© Michael Carroll/Phototake NYC

CHAPTER 6

p. 71—© Sally Bensusen/SPL/PR

CHAPTER 7

p. 83—© David A. Hardy/SPL/PR p. 85—courtesy Carnegie Institution p. 87—courtesy STSCI/NASA/SPL/PR

CHAPTER 8

p. 93—© David A. Hardy/SPL/PR

CHAPTER 9

p. 99—© UPI/BETTMANN p. 100—© Philip Bermingham Photography p. 106—© David Parker/SPL/PR

CHAPTER 10

p. 110—© UPI/BETTMANN p. 113—© Julian Baum/SPL/PR p. 115—courtesy NASA/Science Source/PR